D0211711

What The Experts Say. . .

This handbook will empower you to understand and activate your own immune system. A must read for the stressful 1990s.

–*Eli Bay, Director,*
The Relaxation Response Centre.

The key to developing a healthy immune system is to learn what makes it work in the first place. Understanding the mechanisms involved is crucial if one wishes to optimize health. Thanks to *The Immune System Handbook* the task is made simpler and more fun. Charlene Day, through her step by step approach, gives the reader a clear picture of how the immune system works and how to enhance its actions. As a health care practitioner and educator, I highly recommend this book to anyone.

–*Zoltan P. Rona, M.D., M.Sc.,*
Author of The Joy of Health,
Past President, Canadian Holistic Medical Association.

Your immune system is your ally. For a fascinating explanation of the friendship between your immune system and yourself, you must read this clear and accurate description of their dynamic relationship.

–*Sheila Pennington, Ph.D.,*
Author of Healing Yourself:
Understanding How Your Mind Can Heal Your Body.
Cancer self-help educator.

. . . About This Book

The Immune System Handbook is a readable "instruction manual" for your body's defense department. Charlene Day makes it easy for everyone to understand how their body protects them against disease, and how to help enhance those defenses. . . every human being should have this book.

–Peter G. Hanson, M.D.,
Author of the bestseller The Joy of Stress.

This book divides into three sections–an introduction to the immune system's parts and functions, a dramatization of these parts and their different challenges, and finally an integration of this system into the body and the person as a whole. It will serve as a useful introduction to the immune system.

–J.A. Allen, B.Sc., M.B., B.Ch.

THE IMMUNE SYSTEM

HAND BOOK

YOUR OWNER'S MANUAL

CHARLENE A. DAY

Illustrated by Michael O'Regan

Copyright © 1991 by Charlene Day.

All rights reserved. No part of this book may be reproduced by any means in whole or in part, or stored in a data base or retrieval system or transmitted in any form without prior permission of the publisher, excepting brief quotes used in connection with reviews written specifically for inclusion in a magazine or newspaper.

Address inquiries to the publisher:

Potentials Within
Suite 1839
5334 Yonge St.
North York, Ontario M2N 6M2

Canadian Cataloguing in Publication Data
Day, Charlene A., 1951-
The Immune System Handbook: Your Owner's Manual
Includes bibliographical references and index.
ISBN 0-9695781-0-5
1. Immune System.   I. Title
QR181.7.D3 1991   616.07'9   C92-093109-X

Cover design by Michael O'Regan
Typography by Peter Churchill
Printed and bound in Canada

DEDICATION

I dedicate this book to all the people who have died of AIDS and cancer. Their disease processes have taught us much about our bodies, especially our immune systems, and how much more we have yet to learn.

TABLE OF CONTENTS

Notice

This book is no substitute for the advice of a
doctor. Discuss medical disorders and problems,
injuries and illnesses with a physician.

ACKNOWLEDGMENTS

I offer heartfelt thanks to all my friends who supported me in so many ways.

Special thanks go to:

Michael O'Regan for his creative and original interpretation of the immune system cells.

My wonderfully creative editing team: Grant Fair, Catherine Staples, Steve Chadwick, Peter Kelly, John Gallagher and Laine Williams.

Ron Hernando for routinely setting track records on the word processor.

Bill Day, who backed me through a period of research and to Jean Duncan-Day, who gave constant support and encouragement–without them, this book would not have been.

My appreciative thanks go to my husband, Grant, whose assistance with research, editing, humour, listening, and patience brought the book alive.

FOREWORD

by

Ronald Gold, M.D., M.P.H., Chief, Division of Infectious Disease, The Hospital For Sick Children, Professor of Pediatrics and Microbiology.

The *Immune System Handbook* is an excellent introduction to the human immune system. This enormously complex, interrelated, communicating system of cells, proteins, hormones, and nervous tissue has one basic task: to determine whether a substance or a cell is self or non-self and to remove the latter from the body. The mechanisms by which the immune system recognizes and destroys foreign objects such as bacteria, viruses and other pathogens are vitally important to our health. Equally important are the control systems which regulate the immune system so that it neither over-reacts against invaders, thereby damaging the host, nor misdirects its attack against normal cells. Such loss of control may be at the root of diseases classified as autoimmune disorders such as systemic lupus erythematosis (SLE) and rheumatoid arthritis.

Chapters three to six explain in clear language for the non-scientific reader how the immune system works. The many different types of immune cells, their means of recognizing foreign substances, their methods of communicating information and co-ordinating their activities are presented in a fashion which clearly demonstrates how the immune system defends the body. The chapters which precede and follow are based on controversial studies.

The *Immune System Handbook* is an excellent introduction to a vital part of the human body and the attentive reader will benefit greatly from this work.

PREFACE

Many of us believe that our health is something which only doctors and prescription drugs can influence. We are culturally programmed to expect fast cures for our ills and to look to others for the answers.

This book will show you that there is a powerful healing capacity inside you. This innate intelligence is working constantly to restore the balance and harmony we call health. We do have more control over our health than we have learned. We can participate in our healing and work with our doctors, not against them. The purpose of this book is to show you how to prevent disease and to work with your body if you are experiencing disease.

I am a health care educator. For over twenty years I have explored many healing methods that complement traditional medicine. I have worked with nutrition, stress management, communication skills and personal development. I realize that physical, mental, emotional and spiritual elements are all necessary aspects for healing. Any illness or disease is the result of an imbalance in one or more of these areas.

During the last ten years I have noticed a surge of interest in the desire to maintain peak health. People are more aware that they are responsible for their own health; they are asking more questions and demanding more answers.

It was this interest which led me to a workshop with Jeanne Achterberg. She rekindled my interest in the immune system, not only for myself but for my clients, including those with life-threatening illnesses.

Jeanne is an eminent pioneer and leading researcher/practitioner in the field of psychoneuroimmunology (PNI)—the inquiry into the mind's influence on the immune system. As a creative and trailblazing thinker, she is clearly into healing the planet. I liked her obvious humanity and down-to-earth style.

Her cartoon interpretations of some immune system cells made a lasting impression on me. I realized that this previously obscure and difficult subject could be explained easily and in an entertaining manner. And, this was really worth explaining!

I left the workshop, excited about relearning the dynamics of the immune system. I started with my old physiology texts and some library books. I found that most of the books were complex and I realized that unless readers had some basic knowledge of physiology, they would have some difficulty. I was unable to get the idea of the cartoons out of my head as I felt they would be a great teaching vehicle. I researched the immune system and explained the function of every known cell to an artist. By June 1990 I had an immune system slide show, with immune cell caricatures.

When I presented the slide show, people requested something tangible they could take home with them. The result is this book. I hope it makes your immune system easy to understand and care for.

INTRODUCTION

T *cell. Macrophage*. What images do these words conjure up for you? Perhaps the same nervousness, confusion or blankness you felt when you first read about disk drives, DOS, megabytes or floppies in your computer manual.

This book is about your immune system. We have manuals for our cars. We have manuals for VCRs and computers. So why not a manual for our own bodies? Once you know how your immune system works it may be easier for you to stay healthy. Knowledge is power when it comes to the immune system— even if you believe when all else fails, read the manual!

Remember how you felt when someone told you exactly how to get that dumb computer to work, after you spent hours watching the computer do nothing? Or someone arrived who understood what needed fixing after your car "died"? I want **you** to be that someone when it comes to your immune system. It is my fervent hope that when you have finished this book, when you encounter *T cell* or *macrophage*, a memorable image will spring to mind. And that the picture will contain understanding and meaning for you, as much as any picture of well known family members or friends.

One last note—the artist and I chose military characters to illustrate the immune system because they were simply the best model to explain a system that is mobilized to defend and acts like an army. The illustrations are teaching aids only; if you find better images to understand the immune system, great! In fact, if you are going to visualize healing in your body then the images you find yourself are the best.

The Immune System Handbook

Chapter 1

THE MAGNIFICENT HUMAN BODY

We usually see our body as a collection of many parts like arms, legs, trunk and head; simple components connected together. From this viewpoint, it may be difficult to imagine that the human body consists of over 70 trillion cells, spaces between the cells, and body fluids, all contained within an organ called the skin.

Cells are the basic unit of the body. They group together to form tissues. Examples of tissues include fingernail, adenoid, and brain tissues. Tissues form the framework for the organs and in turn the organs group together to form systems. Examples of systems are: the reproductive system, the digestive system, the nervous system, the endocrine system and the immune system. These and other systems usually act together synergistically. They have a common purpose—keeping the body functioning normally and in good health.

Each cell in the body has a mind of its own. It knows how to create the patterns, interconnections, symmetries and transformations which maintain our body. Each one contains a complete genetic blueprint for constructing an entire body, but we are talking about more than this. Cells have memory, they respond to stimuli, and they are able to distinguish amongst themselves. Cells are able to regulate essential functions and communicate between systems. So it is important to

1

realize that your mind or intelligence is not confined solely to the brain, but permeates your entire being.

Cells go through constant change. We discard dead skin cells every day. The skin we see right now is different from the skin we had last month. Our bones seem solid but we actually acquire a new skeleton every three months on a molecular level. There is much more renewal than medicine previously recognized. All of the cells in our bodies (except those in the central nervous system) are replaced at least every seven years. We are always in process.

Another important aspect of the body is this: it sustains homeostasis—a state of equilibrium or physiological balance within the body. This means the body is always doing its best to maintain the internal balance needed to live. If we become too hot, the body will regulate itself and we will sweat until the temperature is back to normal. Normal may be different for everyone; it is the point each body returns to most of the time.

In terms of healing, the body always wants to be in a state of balance. When we cut ourselves, the body heals the cut without any conscious effort on our part. The body is then back to normal. This is true of the disease process as well. The immune system is always working with all the other systems toward putting the body back into balance.

Chapter 2

THE BODY/MIND CONNECTION

A new specialty is emerging. It is called psychoneuroimmunology, the study of how thoughts and feelings (psycho) interact with your nervous system (neuro) to promote healing (immunology).

In the last decade, exciting research has greatly expanded our understanding of the immune system. Scientists have begun to unravel exactly how stress and mental or emotional states (positive or negative) interact with the immune system. These states can influence the onset and course of disease. Studies show that emotions, which trigger a chemical event in the brain, can affect nervous system function, hormone levels (the endocrine system) and immune system responses. This may make people more (or less) vulnerable to a host of illnesses.

Using a language of biochemicals and nerves, the mind and body communicate constantly. The mind plays an important role in protecting us from disease, or helping us to recover. Research shows that brain chemicals can change thoughts. Thoughts, attitudes, beliefs, values, memories and moods can change the chemicals—and how well we feel and function. Jeanne Achterberg, in her book *Imagery in Healing*, states: "The point is, the body/mind responds as a unit. No thought, no emotion, is without biochemical, electrochemical activity; and the activity leaves no cell untouched."

We can gain more control over the voluntary and involuntary functions of our bodies than was formerly believed. Yoga masters can raise their heart rate from 80 to 300 beats per minute and raise their body temperature sufficiently to melt snow. The techniques they use are made up of detailed visualizations. The rest of us ordinary mortals can attain control over body temperature, blood pressure, heart rate, muscle tension, etc., through the use of biofeedback.

Biofeedback literally means the continual monitoring (receiving) and sending of bodily information back to the brain using various instruments. Biofeedback devices are usually electronic transducers and amplifiers, which allow you to use the information as feedback to actually alter biological functions in your body.

For example, an electrode placed on your tense forehead relays the changing tension in the muscles. Depending on the type of instrument used, you may hear a sound or see a meter as the tension changes. With repetition, you would be able to associate muscle relaxation with a change in sound or needle position. In this way you could learn to gain voluntary control over biological functions normally considered to be under involuntary control.

Elmer and Alyce Green of the Menninger Clinic believe that "biofeedback clearly demonstrates the physiological principle that every change in the physiological state is accompanied by an appropriate change in the mental emotional state, conscious or unconscious, and conversely, every change in the mental emotional state, conscious or unconscious, is accompanied by an appropriate change in the physiological state."

As well as biofeedback, perhaps the simplest form of human learning, classical conditioning, can also affect body function. Psychologist Robert Ader and immunologist Nicholas Cohen found that suppression of the immune system can be conditioned. They repeatedly gave a group of rats saccharin water containing an immunosuppressant drug. Later they gave these rats plain saccharin water, with no drug. The rats' immune systems were suppressed anyway, just as if they had been given the drugged water. Their immune responses had been conditioned to the sweet taste of saccharin. In another experiment, Dr. Novera Herbert Spector conditioned mice to increase their immune responses when exposed to the smell of camphor.

There is nothing innately suppressive or positive about saccharin or camphor—any neutral stimulus could have been used. The fascinating point is that immune system response can be learned through classical conditioning. We know that many classically conditioned responses, including emotional responses and internal bodily functions can sometimes be modified by more complex kinds of learning. This more complex learning includes changes in thinking, attitudes, understanding, and beliefs. These may result from a whole range of experiences including education through to trance or hypnotic learnings.

As Norman Cousins says in Kenneth Pelletier's book *Holistic Medicine*, "Enough verifiable data have appeared about the ability of the human mind to play a major role in overcoming illness to make this entire field enormously attractive to laymen...the biochemical manifestations of mental powers are being well documented. But systematic scrutiny of such phenomena, however, has lagged behind popular interest, the result being that the entire field has been somewhat coloured by guess work and extraordinary claims. Out of it all, however, has emerged the undeniable evidence that the human mind can be trained to play an important part in both preventing disease and in overcoming it when it occurs."

The body/mind connection incorporates many interactions. Here we are going to highlight the relationship between the nervous, endocrine and immune systems. These systems may be so closely linked that they are actually a single network. We know that the immune system and the nervous system share biochemicals. These appear to send information back and forth to each other. Some immune cells have receptors on their membranes for neuropeptides (chemicals produced by the brain) and for neurotransmitters (chemicals released from nerve endings). Also, some immune cells have surface receptors for hormones secreted from the endocrine glands.

Let's use the stress response as an example of body/mind interaction. The chain of reactions starts with the hypothalamus (part of the brain). It activates, controls and integrates autonomic (involuntary) mechanisms. This includes the nervous systems for activity (sympathetic) and relaxation (parasympathetic). It also regulates endocrine activities, and many other bodily functions, such as temperature.

When we experience some kind of perceived stress, either mentally or physically, the hypothalamus releases a chemical. This induces the pituitary gland (the master gland of the endocrine system) to secrete a hormone. That, in turn, orders the adrenal glands to release steroid hormones. This stimulates the autonomic part of our nervous system.

The autonomic nervous system is divided into two parts: the sympathetic and the parasympathetic systems. There is some overlap of functions, but basically these systems operate at different times. So under stress, the sympathetic portion of the autonomic nervous system is activated. This produces a general condition of heightened arousal. Heart rate increases, blood pressure increases, breathing changes, digestion shuts down, blood is pumped to the arms and legs, pupils dilate, etc. Other endocrine glands (besides the adrenals and pituitary) also are involved. The pancreas secretes insulin in response to increased blood sugar. The functioning of the thymus gland, also part of the immune system, may be inhibited. This entire response is known as the fight, fright or flight syndrome.

Let's continue with this lengthy chain of body/mind reactions to stress. The steroids from the adrenals also block the production of the communication chemicals of the immune system. In small doses, steroid hormones spur the immune response. But in constant doses, the steroid hormones suppress the immune response. Under stress, steroids tell the immune system (through surface receptors for hormones), to stop functioning.

We see that the immune system is sensitive to endocrine influences, especially adrenal hormones. It also reacts to nervous influences when the sympathetic nervous system is activated. So stress gets the brain (nervous system), endocrine system and immune system all communicating. This produces the bodily changes we associate with the stress response. Our chain of reactions is finally complete.

Another important body/mind example is relaxation. When the hypothalamus activates the parasympathetic nervous system, it prepares the body for more sedentary activities. These include sleep, relaxation and meditation. Most parasympathetic responses are opposite to sympathetic system responses. In other words, you can't relax and run at the same time! The parasympathetic rest and repair syndrome is activated when balance or homeostasis is required. Parasympathetic function must predominate before healing takes place. Most of us tend to lead lifestyles which don't allow us enough rest and repair.

Chapter 3

YOUR IMMUNE SYSTEM

W hy do we have immune systems? Whether the immune system evolved originally to protect us from infectious invaders, to monitor inside us for mutant cells, or to regulate the body's other systems, it has brought with it enormous advantages.

The immune system, in simple terms, is a group of bio-chemicals, cells, tissues and organs strategically located throughout the body. Constantly challenged, these cells work together, detecting any foreign substance in the body, defending and abolishing what does not belong.

At least a thousand times a day, clusters of bacteria, viruses, fungi, parasites, allergens and other assorted micro-organisms try to invade the body. We ingest a bacteria; we pick up a fungus; we inhale a pollen. Not all of these micro-organisms are hostile. Some of these microbes live in us and others live on us. Others directly benefit us. They grow, reproduce and feed on what we discard. But those that do pose a threat are usually destroyed, routinely, quietly and unknown to us.

The immune system is naive at first; it educates itself through each exposure to each new and unknown invader. Without this system we could not survive. When it malfunctions, we are vulnerable to a huge variety of diseases from allergy to arthritis to cancer.

If you have an excellent genetic composition, you will probably enjoy a good natural defense against infections and diseases. You may stay healthy in spite of yourself, even if you are a heavy smoker, heavy drinker or poor eater.

Most of us carry within our bodies organisms, which if left unchallenged, would destroy us. They often live near us in a kind of stand-off relationship. They can overpower us if we are injured or weakened by stress, exhaustion or malnutrition. Then the delicate balance is upset. We become vulnerable to their attack and the many illnesses they unleash.

When the immune system functions normally, it can tell whether out-of-body invaders *belong* inside you or not. When a foreign invader enters the bloodstream, it has surface markers. These markers fit perfectly with certain immune system cells like a key fits in a lock. This lets the immune system, in effect, *fingerprint* the invader cell which in turn allows the immune system to distinguish *self* from *non-self*. *Non-self* can be viral, bacterial, fungal, parasitic, chemical or even a portion or product of one of these organisms.

Tissues or cells from another individual (except identical twins) also act as non-self. The immune system recognizes transplanted tissues as foreign and it rejects them. The body will even reject nourishing proteins unless they are first broken down by the digestive system into their primary, non-invader building blocks. As cells of the immune system patrol the body, they seek any particle that does not have the self marker.

The immune system can identify the precise nature of millions of intruders. Once it detects the intruders, it sets in motion a complex chain reaction designed to produce specific weapons to fight each of them. It is also designed to protect the body from further attack.

Have you ever wondered why some of us get sick and some of us don't? Or why do some of us get better very quickly, while some of us are sick for longer periods of time? We are all exposed to the same viruses and bacteria, yet our immune systems handle the invasions differently. The answers to why our immune systems are different seem to lie at the cellular level of the body. Several factors contribute to immune functioning.

Firstly, we all have different genetic material that makes up our immune systems. Secondly, our cells must be cared for, nourished and maintained in a proper biochemical environment. Cells can be strengthened by natural food, good water and air, sleep, relaxation, breathing, exercise, good mental and emotional health, and a sense of purpose—a spiritual connection. Cells are nourished by vitamins, minerals and trace elements, amino acids, carbohydrates and essential fatty acids.

Thirdly, our cells must be protected from today's environmental pollution, dietary stresses and stressful lifestyle which frustrate and damage cellular function. These enemies of good health may make us more vulnerable, thereby allowing other undesirables to take over.

Chapters 7 and 8 further describe these friends and enemies of the immune system.

Chapter 4

A QUICK TOUR OF YOUR IMMUNE SYSTEM

I magine shrinking yourself down to the size of a tiny cell in order to travel inside your body. Each cell in your body bears a marker that is unique to you. It identifies your cells as self. This marker is like a fingerprint that is made up of several molecules in a distinct pattern. No one else's cells have the same marker, except identical twins. So as you travel through your body, your immune system recognizes you and you are able to travel as you please. If it doesn't recognize you, you'll be attacked.

Our tour will be quick, and you will meet many, but not all characters of the immune system. Because you have had so little concrete experience with your immune system parts, the system may seem a little abstract. Don't worry. Think of meeting a large contingent of a friend's family at a family reunion. Unless your memory is exceptional, you will be glad if you can remember just a few faces and names at the end of the day. This tour is designed to get you into the ball park, not to make you a baseball expert. Later chapters and illustrations will make them clearer and more memorable. Please feel free to return to look at the illustrations as you read the text.

The body's first level of defense is the covering: the skin, mucous membranes, and linings of the digestive tract and airways. We have to go past the skin, so we will enter through

CELLS OF THE IMMUNE SYSTEM

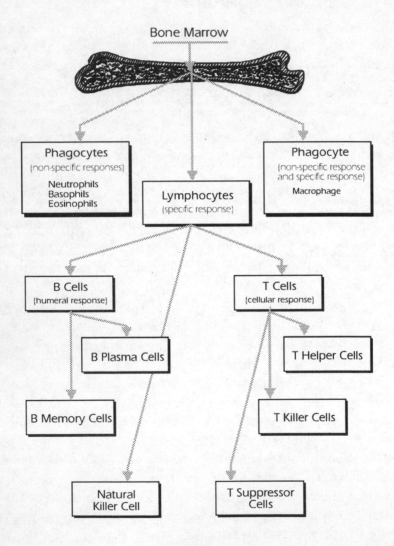

Figure 1

the mouth or the nose. All the entrances to the body–nostrils, mouth, eyes, ears, genitals and anus–have their own protective devices.

If we enter the nostrils going to the respiratory tract, we discover a lining of cells with hair-like projections called cilia. The cilia move in a wave-like motion. There is mucous secreted here in order to catch foreign invaders. The cilia direct the invader upward toward the throat where coughing dislodges it.

If we enter via the mouth, we are met with saliva which harbours strong enzymes capable of resisting infections. If we were unwanted invaders and were swallowed, we would be destroyed by hydrochloric acid acting as a sterilizing agent in the stomach.

If we enter through the eyes, we see that tears contain chemicals that kill invaders. These chemicals also wash dirt and dust out of the eyes.

Before our tour begins, let's note that the immune system has no single central location in the body, and no chief organ. Instead, it is a co-operative system of biochemicals and white blood cells (leukocytes), tissues and organs which are distributed throughout the body in various locations.

Let's also note two locations which are essential to the immune system. If you take a look at *Figure 1* now, it will give you an overview of all white blood cells produced in the bone marrow. From the bone marrow, some white cells are sent to the thymus gland for training. *Figure 2* (over the page) shows the location of the thymus in your body.

Bone marrow is the soft tissue in the hollow shafts of the long bones such as those in your arms and legs. All blood cells, both red and the immune system's white, are produced in the bone marrow. All blood cells start as a stem cell (a basic

THE LYMPHATIC SYSTEM

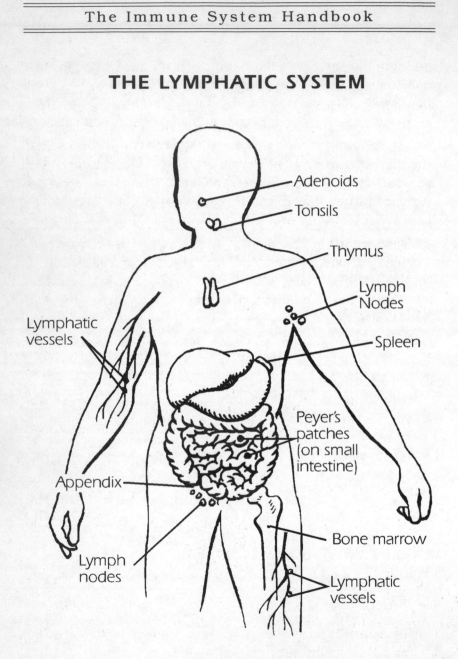

Figure 2

building block cell) and develop into groups of more specific secondary stem cells. The secondary cells produce different families of cells, some red and some white. Our tour will focus on the white cells alone, as they make up the immune system.

All white blood cells can be divided into two groups. One of these groups are *generalists* which respond to general kinds of threats, such as cuts. These are the phagocytes. The other group are *specialists*. Each responds to a very specific invader; this group is the lymphocytes. These specialist lymphocytes are stored in the spleen, lymph nodes, tonsils, adenoids, appendix, and clusters of lymphoid tissue in the wall of the intestine called Peyer's patches.

The Phagocytes:
Mac and the Phil Brothers

Phago means *eater* or *that which devours*. Phagocytes are particle-devouring white cells. Like ravenous Cookie Monsters, they roam the body looking for *invader-cookies* to munch on. There are two kinds of phagocytes. One is the macrophage. The others include what I call the *Phil Brothers*–neutrophils, basophils, and eosinophils.

The Lymphocytes:
Bs, Ts, and Natural Killer Cells

As the lymphocytes develop, they divide into B cells and T cells. As they separate, B cells and T cells follow different pathways to populate your body with the various kinds of blood cells it needs. There are two kinds of B cells, and three kinds of T cells. There is some evidence for additional kinds of lymphocytes, such as natural killer cells. (There may be additional cells, but they are yet to be clearly identified and named.)

OUR TOUR BEGINS

Let's begin our tour by visiting some bone marrow. As mentioned before, bone marrow is the origin of all immune cells. B cells complete their maturation in the bone marrow.

T cells, on the other hand, migrate to the thymus, which we will now tour. The thymus is a greyish organ with two lobes, sitting behind the breast bone, near the heart. It is part of the endocrine system. Incidentally, some writers suggest there is clinical evidence that production of T cells can be stimulated by tapping the breast bone. This stimulates thymus hormones, which in turn stimulates T cell production.

We see that the thymus is a training centre for inexperienced T cells. The thymus produces several hormones which are used to train T cells. They are trained to distinguish self cells from non-self cells; T cells that would react against self markers are abolished. Here the T cells multiply and reach maturity. This training is particularly essential to the development of the immune response in newborns.

Let us follow some B cells and T cells as they exit the bone marrow and thymus. Some of these cells gather in immune organs like the spleen or tonsils or they stay in the lymph nodes. Others travel widely and continuously throughout the body via the blood circulation and the lymph system.

Lymph is a clear and colourless fluid that is collected from tissue in all parts of the body. It is then returned to the blood by way of the lymphatic system. Lymph contains many different proteins, salts, organic substances and water. The lymph system has ducts and tissues which convey the lymph fluid from the body's tissues to the bloodstream. Unlike our blood circulation system, which has a pump (the heart) and valves in the veins to ensure blood circulation, the lymph system depends entirely on muscular activity and deep breathing to keep the lymph moving.

As we travel through this system, we see that it includes capillaries, nodes, vessels and ducts. The lymph acts as a cleanser by collecting harmful substances from these tissue spaces and transporting them across the thin walls of tiny lymphatic vessels. The vessels transport the mix to lymph nodes, where foreign matter, debris, unwanted micro-organisms and dust particles are filtered out. Anything unwanted is presented to immune cells.

The bean-shaped lymph nodes are located along the lymphatic routes—with clusters in the neck, armpits, abdomen, and groin. During flu, a cold, or after a tooth extraction, you may have noticed swelling in some of these lymph areas —evidence that your immune system was hard at work protecting you.

Each lymph node contains specialized compartments. Each compartment has platoons of B cells, T cells and other cells capable of trapping the invader and presenting it to T cells. Once their job is done, the lymph is cleared of invaders. Then the lymph fluid makes its way to the base of the neck where large lymphatic vessels funnel into the thoracic duct.

The thoracic duct empties its contents into the bloodstream. Once in the bloodstream, the lymphocytes and other assorted immune cells are transported to tissues throughout the body. They patrol everywhere for foreign invaders, then gradually drift back into the lymphatic vessels, and begin the cycle again.

As we complete our tour, we find another location where many T and B cells gather, in the spleen. It is a fist-sized organ at the upper left of the abdomen. Here, many elements of invading organisms are filtered out of the circulating blood system. They are presented to the immune system, allowing it to respond in very specific ways that will provide protection against disease or infection.

The spleen also screens out ineffective or exhausted blood cells of the immune system. It contains two main types of tissue. The red pulp, where worn-out blood cells are disposed; and the white pulp, which contains lymphoid tissue. Like the lymph nodes, the spleen's lymphoid tissue is subdivided into compartments that specialize in a variety of immune cells. Micro-organisms carried by the blood into the red pulp become trapped by the immune cells known as macrophages. (Although people can live without a spleen, persons whose spleens have been damaged by trauma or disease are highly susceptible to infection).

We have now visited the major locations where we would find immune system cells. Now, let's watch some action. If we were to watch when the body is invaded, we would see that the lymphocytes (T cells and B cells) and the phagocytes (Mac and the Phil Brothers) respond in different ways: one specifically and one nonspecifically. Before we see that though, we need to understand two terms: humoral immunity and cellular immunity.

Humoral Immunity:

B cells

B cells work chiefly by secreting soluble substances called antibodies into the body's fluids. This results in humoral immunity (humor simply means fluid). Antibodies typically interact with invaders that circulate in the body's fluids, but are unable to penetrate living cells. Antibodies act like guided missiles on a seek and destroy mission.

Cellular Immunity:
T cells and friends

Some invaders such as viruses are able to penetrate the walls of the cell, so the function of the T cells is to directly attack damaged body cells. This is called cellular immunity and it involves the recruitment of phagocytes, killer T cells, and natural killer cells.

Nonspecific Response & the Phagocyte Generalists

The nonspecific healing response involves inflammation –the familiar swelling and reddening of the skin in response to cuts, abrasions, punctures, burns or diseases of the skin. It is the job of macrophages and the Phil Brothers, and something called the complement proteins (see page 38 for more details) to repair the damaged tissue. This healing process does not involve stimulation of antibodies, as there is no recognition of a particular invader. The nonspecific healing process often requires the co-operation of antibodies and lymphocytes in reaction to specific invaders, like viruses.

Specific Response & Lymphocyte Specialists

The specific healing response is activated when the body remembers a particular invader such as the measles virus. It is more complex than the nonspecific response. We see that it involves cellular and humoral immunity responses (those terms we just learned). It is called specific because each lymphocyte and each antibody respond only to one specific invader. This specific response is the hallmark of the immune system. The specific healing response generates immunologic memory of the foreign invader that triggers the response. Should that foreign invader attack the body again, the specific

CELLS OF THE IMMUNE SYSTEM

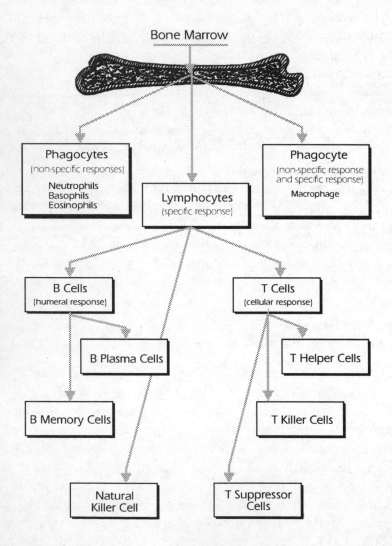

healing response will occur more rapidly and with greater force. It seems that the immune system recognizes and remembers the identity of specific invaders, after they have met once, as well as how to defeat them.

In some disease states, the specific response can become chronic and destructive, but usually both specific and nonspecific responses are powerful strategies for defense. The specific immune responses (humoral and cellular) and the nonspecific immune responses work sequentially and harmoniously to recognize, attack and destroy invaders.

Summary

This quick tour should give you an overall picture of the immune system. Not all of the details about the white blood cells and their origin have been included, but in the next chapter, you will have a chance to meet the many specific characters of the immune system. You will find out more about each of these spectacular friends of the body.

Chapter 5

GOOD GUYS AND BAD GUYS:

The Immune System and
its Cellular Enemies

Your body contains 25 trillion red blood cells and for every 1000 red blood cells there is a white blood cell, or leukocyte. A drop of your blood contains 5 million red cells and 5,000 to 10,000 white cells. All white blood cells begin in the bone marrow, born from stem cells. White blood cells are made up of several different groups of cells. Each group is highly specialized. Leukocytes are divided into the generalist phagocytes, specialist lymphocytes and natural killer cells. They all recognize and eliminate foreign matter. They interact with each other to aid and enhance the activities of every other cell.

In the last chapter, we saw that the white blood cells circulate in the bloodstream, travelling through arteries, veins and capillaries. As well, they often flow through the lymphatic system, before returning to the circulatory system. Other cells stay in the lymphatic tissue, or in organs like the spleen, lymph nodes, the adenoids or tonsils until they are needed to fight an infection.

Now you will meet the main characters of the immune system. Each individual white blood cell will come alive as you understand its function.

THE GOOD GUYS

PHAGOCYTES:

(Neutrophils, Basophils, Eosinophils & Macrophages)

These are the generalists who provide nonspecific responses. For example, they respond to cuts, abrasions, punctures, burns, infections, or diseases of the skin.

The Phil Brothers:
(Neutrophils, Basophils, Eosinophils)

Neutrophils

These are the *front-line* foot soldiers, the *mass infantry* of the body's defenses. They make up 62% of white blood cells and have a short life span. They are constantly active in healthy persons on a day-to-day basis. They attack and destroy bacteria and engulf harmful micro-organisms. They do the same for lifeless particles like asbestos and cellular debris. They attack and destroy foreign invaders before the activation of antibody formation. They get rid of virus particles that have already been attacked by antibodies.

Neutrophils produce small proteins which help defend against bacteria, fungi and several viruses. These proteins function like antibiotics, although they are chemically quite distinct from any known antibiotics.

When chemicals are released at the site of injury, the neutrophils prepare for attack by changing shape. Their new shape helps them get through the vessel walls to do their work. They adhere to the walls of the capillaries, which have become sticky just for that purpose. They extend a small foot called a *pseudopod* (false foot) through any convenient gap. Once out of the blood stream, they move toward the offender and begin the process of destruction.

This engulfment and digestion is called phagocytosis. Neutrophils send their cytoplasm (glue-like fluid) flowing around the foreign particle to surround it. Then they isolate it in a sac (called a phagosome). They shoot enzymes into the sac, and the invader is destroyed!

Eventually the neutrophil is destroyed too. But since 100 billion neutrophils are produced a day, the loss is normally insignificant. When they destroy invaders, they exude biochemicals into the blood. These trigger local inflammation and summon other defensive cells to action.

Basophils

Basophils are like a *suicide squad*; they are *specialized forces*. They make up 0.4% of white blood cells and play an important role in some types of allergic reactions. If you are a hayfever sufferer, or suffer from allergic reactions, you can thank the basophils.

Basophils have a special preference to become attached to an antibody called IgE. Antibodies, you will remember, are like guided missiles. The IgE an-tibody causes allergic reactions. IgE also attaches to another cell called a mast cell. The mast cell is almost the same as the basophil. However, mast cells are located in the tissues, while the basophil circulates in the blood. Mast cells are found in the linings of the respiratory and digestive tracts.

When the specific invader reacts with the antibody IgE, the resulting attachment of the invader to the antibody causes the mast cell or basophil to rupture. It then releases exceedingly large quantities of histamine, bradykinin, and serotonin. These substances have several functions, including opening up blood vessels (thus causing the typical swelling of nasal passages in hayfever).

This outwardly annoying symptom allows the inner work of the immune system to proceed more quickly and efficiently as it allows the basophils to get though the capillaries. These substances also communicate with various systems such as the nervous system or endocrine system. Lysosomal enzymes, (which attack bacteria and cause them to disintegrate) are also released. These in turn cause vascular and tissue reactions, such as the reddening of the skin and other allergic manifestations.

Basophils also release heparin into the blood. Heparin is a substance that prevents blood coagulation. It can also speed the removal of fat particles from the blood after a fatty meal.

Eosinophils

Eosinophils are like *infantry specialists*. These cells are among the front-line troops of the immune system and make up 2.3% of white blood cells. They are accessory cells which gather at the site of infection.

Eosinophils appear to protect self tissues from other immune elements, such as inflammatory chemicals released by the neutrophils. They are known to secrete an enzyme which is capable of deactivating histamine. They have the ability to devour whatever originally caused the allergic reaction. Their number increases in response to allergies, coughs, parasitic infections, malaise, etc. They are more active in persons suffering from anorexia nervosa, a psychological disturbance marked by severe weight loss.

Macrophages

They are among the *front-line* troops. They are like the *Signal Corps* in that they signal, and call for reinforcements. They make up 5.3% of white blood cells and they are sometimes called the *big eaters*. They are called monocytes when they are circulating in the blood. When they are found in fluid around inflammation, they begin to swell; then they are called macrophages.

Macrophage

Macrophages look for invaders in the blood. They scavenge and digest invaders, and patrol the body mopping up debris. They eat anything not marked self. They eat defunct red blood cells and look for substances that don't belong in the body. What they can't eat, they cover and store. One macrophage can swallow as many as 100 invaders. Macrophages collect in the walls of the intestines, and in the central nervous system, liver, spleen, lungs, lymph nodes, bone marrow and connective tissue. Here they become mobilized when stimulated by inflammation.

Macrophages attack invaders, engulf and then devour them. The macrophage doesn't recognize what kind of invader it is. All it knows is that the invader doesn't belong to the body. Once the invader is digested, the macrophage spits up a tiny bit of it, and displays it like a flag on its surface.

This isn't bad manners, it's good immunology. It triggers a series of events. First, T helper cells are alerted. Then, when the appropriate T helper cell recognizes the flag, it locks together with the macrophage. The macrophage then secretes a hormone, which results in fever. (Great, you think - I'm fighting invaders and my immune system gives me a fever!) Actually, this is health promoting. The fever creates a hostile atmosphere for the invader. It also activates T helper cells, causing them to reproduce at the site of infection. The macrophage contains enzymes which enable it to digest almost any living matter it devours. Mac will eat anything!

LYMPHOCYTES:
(T Cells & B Cells)

The lymphocytes are active in specific responses, which involve both cellular and humoral immune responses. They make up 30% of white blood cells.

T Cells:
(Cellular immune response)

T-4 Helper or T Helper Cells

These cells are the *Commanding Officers* of the defense system. T helper cells send signals to all other immune cells. They spur the immune system to battle. They are responsible for sending instructions to all groups of cells engaged in immune response.

T helper cells have specific training in the thymus so they each recognize different invaders. For example, T helper cells are trained and programmed to recognize the measles virus. They have receptors on their surface which fit the pattern of the measles virus on the surface of the macrophage. They recognize the macrophage as self and the flag as non-self. The T helper cell is incapable of seeing the measles virus before this, but in the context of the macrophage, it recognizes it immediately.

The macrophage and the T helper cells lock into one another. The macrophage begins secreting a hormone, which causes fever in the body and creates a hostile atmosphere for the viruses. This stimulates the T helper cell to reproduce, or clone itself and to become effective. The T helper cell doesn't actually engage in destruction of the viruses.

Some T helper clones stay at the site of the invasion. Others travel through the blood stream, the spleen and the nearest lymph nodes. They send hormone signals to B cells and to other members of T cell family. The T helpers also produce signals which regulate the extent and speed with which activities proceed.

T Killer Cells

These cells are the *commando units* which destroy virus-infected cells directly. They mature and train in the thymus.

They are stored in lymph nodes and the spleen. The hormone that stimulates them to grow and reproduce will only stimulate the one programmed for a particular virus.

They are activated by a signal from the T helper cell. With this signal, they latch on to infected cells and puncture the cell membrane with special proteins. They inject time-released poisonous granules which blow up the infected cell before the virus inside has had time to multiply. The whole cell, along with the macrophage, is sacrificed to control the infection. Viruses spilling out after the attack are targets for the macrophages and antibodies waiting there.

Once the infected cells are all gone, T killer cells stop growing and dividing and they die.

Natural Killer Cells

Natural Killer cell

These cells are the *Special Air Services*, the highly trained *elite commando forces* called to deal with tricky situations. These cells circulate in the body and live in lymph nodes. They look like lymphocytes, but probably have a separate ancestry. They do not have enough physical characteristics in common with T or B cells to be grouped in either family. We know more about the function of these cells than we do about their origin.

One group of killer cells have the ability to kill cells that have been coated with antibodies. They are called antibody-dependent killer cells.

Another group, natural killer cells play a significant role against a variety of viral infections. This includes herpes and virus-produced cancers. They are known especially for their activity against cancer cells. It appears they have the ability to kill certain organisms and cells without any help from other sections of the immune system. They appear to work more efficiently in the presence of chemicals released by activated T cells.

While T cells recognize and bind to an invader only when it is introduced by one of a group of surface molecules through the macrophages, natural killer cells are not restricted by the group of surface molecules.

T Suppressor Cells

T suppressor cells are the *military police* that restore the immune system to a state of rest after an invader is defeated.

These cells mature and train in the thymus. They send messages to other T and B cells to slow down and eventually halt their activities. They prevent the immune response from spiralling out of control. T suppressor cells are not the only mechanism for controlling immune system response. Antibody production, for example, can be inhibited by circulating monocytes or macrophages.

B CELLS:
(Humoral Immune Response)
B Plasma Cells

These cells could be called the *war workers*. They, too, mature in the bone marrow and then migrate to the spleen and lymph nodes. B cells become plasma cells when called to action by activated T helper cells. They produce antibodies to fight invaders.

There is a unique B cell to fight each and every different invader. Each B cell is programmed to make only one type of antibody, and each antibody has a receptor only for its own particular invader. Individual B cells become specialized before even meeting an invader. The only B cell stimulated into action is the one whose antibody matches that of the invader.

The B cell divides, making genetically identical copies or clones of itself. Each clone becomes an antibody-producing factory. At the height of activity, B cells produce 2,000 antibodies per second. Antibodies spot invaders such as bacteria, viruses, toxins and particles of dust.

Antibodies produce two kinds of complex protein molecules. The first kind are antibody molecules which move around and through blood and lymph. The second kind are B cell receptors which stay rooted on the B cell's surface membrane. They only live for a few weeks at most.

Antibodies or Immunoglobulins

The antibodies travel through the body like *guided missiles* searching for invaders. They are protein molecules—four strands of amino acids twisted together in a 'Y' shape. The body is capable of making an infinite variety of them. An antibody will match only one specific invader and this precision is the hallmark of our immune system. Antibodies develop only when faced with a particular virus, for example. Resistance to further viral infection therefore depends on first catching that particular virus. The virus *educates* the immune system, training the cells of the body to be prepared for a later attack.

The arms of the 'Y' of the antibody attach to two invaders. Once the antibody interlocks with the invader, it is marked for destruction. Since they cannot penetrate the cells of the body to seek infectious agents, they are only effective against invaders in body fluids. They react by attaching to and neutralizing the invader, blocking its entry into the cell. The antibody may also coat the invaders with a substance that makes them tasty morsels for the macrophage or the antibody-dependent killer cells.

Another strategy of the antibody is pulling invaders into a clump and calling on a series of complement proteins which then destroy the invaders by poking holes into their cell membranes.

There are five classes of antibodies and there are unique antibodies within each class.

IgA antibodies are found chiefly in body secretions such as saliva, tears, and nasal fluids. Secreted along mucous membranes, IgA has the ability to neutralize invading viruses before they can enter the body. IgA in mother's milk provide the first line of defense for babies who breast feed. While they are found chiefly in mucous membranes, IgA are also found in the bloodstream.

IgG antibodies account for about three-quarters of the antibodies present in the bloodstream. Once it attaches to an invader, IgG is important in activating the complement protein. IgG is the only class of antibody that can cross the placenta. Thus, it plays a major role in protecting the fetus. Small amounts of IgG pass to the newborn through mother's milk. IgG can attack and destroy most bacteria.

IgM antibodies are extremely efficient in activating the complement proteins. A single IgM molecule, binding itself to the surface of an invader, can activate all the complement proteins. It is a larger antibody than IgG and must stay in circulation. It can't wiggle through the walls of blood vessels like the IgG can. Curiously, once a B cell has switched from the production of IgM to IgG, it cannot go back to producing IgM. For unknown reasons, B cell production of antibodies can go forward only through a repetitious pattern of immunoglobulin classes.

IgD antibodies are something of an mystery. They are more plentiful than IgM. Their function in immune responses has not yet been identified. They exist on the surface of B cells living in the spleen. When B cells turn on to produce antibodies, they shut off production of IgD and begin secreting other antibodies. IgD may be involved in B cell growth and maturation, but their exact function is not fully understood. They are found in trace amounts in human blood serum.

IgE antibodies are important in triggering allergic reactions. This antibody locks on to mast cells and basophils which have attached themselves to invaders. Here they release histamine, which produces inflammation of the tissues, and enlargement of blood vessels. At the same time, they call in the lymphocytes and phagocytes to help fight invaders. Sometimes they overreact to repeated assaults, bringing on allergic reactions such as hay fever, hives, asthma and occasionally, anaphylactic shock. (Anaphylaxis from a bee sting for example, is a severe allergic reaction affecting the whole body and is sometimes fatal.) Another purpose of IgE is to guard the body against parasites (mites and worms).

Complement

Complement proteins are produced by both macrophages and liver cells. There are 18 kinds of complement proteins, although they act as if they are nine functioning segments. On their own, circulating through the bloodstream, individual complement proteins are inert and inactive. They might appear at first glance to have no purpose at all. Until IgM or IgG antibodies latch onto an invader, complement just loafs around.

At that point they move in, and attach themselves to the invaders one at a time. They do this in a particular sequence. When they are all in place, the invader ruptures and dies. Its cell wall is eaten away by the complement protein enzymes. It is a forceful and fast method of defense. It is crucial to the well-being of the body, and it plays an important role in killing bacteria.The complement can also send out a chemical call for help that brings more neutrophils and macrophages to the scene. Without complement, antibodies cannot destroy infectious invaders. They can only put on handcuffs.

Memory B Cells

They are the *internal security system* or *intelligence agency.*

B memory cell

After they mature in the bone marrow, they migrate to the spleen and lymph nodes. Some B cells become memory B cells which act for long-term immunity. They remain in the body after the invader is killed, and are trained to respond immediately if a particular invader enters the body again. Memory B cells will start production of antibodies against the invader. There are also memory T cells and they will immediately activate macrophage and B cells.

With the first exposure, it takes the immune system up to seven days to mount a defense. Next time around, thanks to memory cells, it will be ready within hours. They may take care of the invader so fast, you may never know the germ came back, or feel any symptoms. You are immune to that particular invader. Most white cells are relatively short-lived. Memory cells can live for at least 20 years and some may live as long as you do.

THE BAD GUYS

These invaders to which the immune system responds are also known as antigens. Antigens are any chemicals recognized by the immune system as foreign. Bacteria, viruses, helminths, protozoa, and fungi contain antigens on their surfaces and within their cells.

Bacteria

Bacteria act very much like *saboteurs*. They are single cell organisms and are able to live on their own. They contain a single strand of DNA, all the information necessary to create new bacteria.

Bacteria

Bacteria attack the body by producing strong toxins (poisonous chemicals) that can damage specific cells and tissues. They block the normal function of important substances in blood and tissues, or they interfere with various regulatory systems that control movement of fluids between blood and tissues. There are three types of toxins:

(1) Exotoxins destroy by directly attacking specific cells, tissues and organs. They are released by disease-producing bacteria. Examples are botulism, tetanus and diphtheria.

(2) Endotoxins are subtle. They act indirectly as they occur in the cell walls of bacteria. Endotoxins cause certain immune cells to release substances that induce fever and chills and increase capillary permeability. Examples are typhoid and dysentery.

(3) Toxic enzymes are proteins that are capable of greatly accelerating or inhibiting chemical reactions produced by the bacteria.

Some bacteria is friendly and we do need this kind of harmless bacteria. The normal flora in the small and large intestines consists of such friendly bacteria. They break down the food we eat into useful compounds like vitamins, or digest it. They also reabsorb the essential nutrients from the food that we eat. They are essential to human life, and live in a delicate symbiotic relationship with us.

Viruses

Virus comes from a Latin word meaning "*a poison*". Viruses are inactive most of the time. They are like *sleeper agents*, waiting to be triggered by the right circumstances. They are the smallest micro-organisms known to science and the simplest forms of life. They are little more than a cluster of genes packaged in a protein coat, (known as a capsid). There is some controversy about whether they are truly alive, since they lack the three conditions which commonly characterize living matter. They are unable to feed on their own, grow on their own, or reproduce themselves on their own.

A virus is like an idea, a plan which needs something else to carry it out. That something is a living cell. The virus can only reproduce by entering a living cell; it is a parasite. It exploits the metabolic machinery of the host cell (as in the human body) to make replicas of itself.

The inner core of viral DNA or RNA contains only instructions for copying viruses. Before this happens, the virus has to gain a foothold on the cell. If it can stay on the surface of the cell long enough, it eventually burrows its way into the cell. Once inside, the virus begins to multiply, overpowering the cell's energy and machinery to become a virus producing factory. The virus fills the cells and the newly formed viruses bud out on the surface. The new viruses cause the invaded cell to burst, thereby releasing more viruses into our systems. These, in turn, are ready to infect more cells.

Between 100 to 1,000 viruses can reproduce in one cell. In defense, the infected cell produces a chemical, *interferon*, which signals that a virus is present. This produces a change in the surrounding cells which prevents the virus from reproducing in them, hampering the spread of infection.

In most acute cases, the immune system responds by attacking and destroying the infected cells and invading viruses. Once resolved, the specialized immune cells give permanent immunity to that specific virus.

The virus must attach itself to a specific site on the surface of the cell, called the viral recognition site. If it is not there, the virus has no entry. The cell is resistant to attack. Different cells have different viral recognition sites. For example, nervous tissue recognizes rabies virus, but not the hepatitis virus.

Many of us carry latent viruses within us, such as *herpes simplex* (cold sores), *cytomegalovirus* (salivary gland virus), *Epstein-Barr virus* (mononucleosis). There are hundreds of different viruses that *may* be present in your blood. Only about 10% of viruses have been identified. These viruses can lie dormant in the body for long periods, then suddenly become alive and destructive, under the right (from a virus's point of view) circumstances.

Reactivation may result from a change in the body's internal environment, for instance, a stressful situation or anything that creates imbalance in the body (see Chapter 7). Viruses can undergo genetic changes or mutations, which may alter their behaviour within the body. Some viruses like Epstein-Barr and Herpes 2 can actually incorporate their own genetic material into the DNA of the invaded cell. Even minor modifications to DNA can induce a profound change in the life of an infected cell. For example, it can transform a normal cell into a cancer cell, which separates from its genetic past, then reproduces at an uncontrollable rate. In the case of HIV virus (the cause of AIDS) it converts its RNA into the DNA of the T helper cell, thereby immobilizing the commander of the immune system.

Fungi

Fungi are enemy *front-line attackers* in that their invasion is usually limited to body surfaces and openings. They are single-celled organisms larger than bacteria. They are opportunists. Unless they enter an endangered host, with a few exceptions they do not usually produce disease. They exist in soil, water, vegetation, and even within us on our skin and in

Fungus

our gastro-intestinal tract. You probably recognize them by their common names: yeast and mould. Usually, they are limited to the hair, nails, and the superficial layers of skin, as with athlete's foot.

One fungus, Candida Albicans can live in the mouth, gastro intestinal tract and the vagina. The immune system and friendly bacteria keep the growth of candida and other fungi under control. When the body's defenses are weakened, fungi proliferate and pervade the tissues of the body. People with weak immune systems will be prone to fungal infections of the skin, intestinal tract, lungs or brain.

In *The Yeast Syndrome*, Dr. John Parks Trowbridge hypothesizes that the yeasts build molecules disguised to look similar to hormonal molecules. With this disguise on the surface, the yeast enters the body's cellular communication traffic, causing problems such as sleepless nights and cramps.

Under certain circumstances fungi can be life-threatening. When intestinal bacteria are killed off by antibiotics, contraceptives, steroids or poor diet, a candida infection can spread from the intestines into the blood stream and to other organs, causing fever, shock and in some cases, death.

Protozoa (amoebae)

Protozoa are like enemy *reserve forces*, waiting for the battle to turn in their favour. They are single cell organisms that are opportunists and parasites. Blood parasites such as malaria will die outside of the body unless they are ingested by a mosquito or appropriate insect carrier. Intestinal protozoa exist in a dormant state as a parasitic cyst. Extremely hardy, they survive for long periods outside the body, usually in contaminated soil, water or food. Once eaten, they grow into mature disease-producing protozoa.

Protozoa

The immune system keeps the population of intestinal parasites under control, but a chronic state of ill health may begin. When the immune system is weak, the blood parasites can aid the cause of death. For example, in the rare case of African sleeping sickness, protozoa have evolved devious strategies for eluding the body's immune surveillance system. The protozoa head for the heart or brain, and if untreated, the disease is fatal.

Some protozoa are genetically programmed to alter their surface markers periodically. Each time the body's immune system cells target one set of protozoa for destruction, the tricky protozoa alter their markers and disappear from the view of the immune system. The immune system must then program another set of immune cells to detect the new surface markers and spot the altered protozoa.

Although the immune system constantly gathers its forces, and protozoa constantly shift surface markers, the immune system successfully controls most protozoal infections. Only if the protozoa invade tissues do symptoms appear. As long as their growth is controlled, the body is typically in no danger. They usually pose no threat to life, and they are quite common in the body. If the immune system becomes disabled, as it does with AIDS, these same protozoa sometimes result in fatal infections.

Helminths

The helminths are the *infiltrators* who move deeply into the digestive system. They are parasitic worms which live in human hosts in the intestinal tract, feeding off the body's nutrients. Examples are the tapeworm, blood flukes and roundworms.

White blood cells cannot penetrate the thick, waxy protective coating of the worm. The worms have evolved intricate mechanisms to protect themselves from attack by the immune system. They masquerade as self cells. They gather substances shed from the surfaces of the host cells and drape them around their outer membranes. When the white blood cells come in contact with disguised invaders, they detect only the self markers and do not respond.

Helminth

Before the helminths disguise themselves, the immune system will have had time to generate a response to the organism's original markers. This initial response is not enough to destroy the invader, but allows both the host and worm to survive. The body quickly responds to any new infection by the undisguised helminth, but it cannot destroy the disguised ones. The infection remains chronic, but never reaches a stage where the life of the host is threatened. The worms insure their own survival this way because they cannot live in a dead host.

The mouth of the worm is its one unprotected area. White blood cells and antibodies will attack and destroy the worm if they find its mouth.

SUMMARY

Now that you have met the characters, you will see them in action. These technical terms will be brought to life in the play. On stage, and clearly visible, they provide visualization images. Your task is to visualize your own immune system characters as they work to keep your body free of disease.

Chapter 6

THE PLAY

Cast Of Characters

The Good Guys

The Phil Brothers
  Neutrophils, Basophils and Eosinophils

Macrophages

T-4 Helper or T Helper Cells

T Killer Cells

Natural Killer Cells

T Suppressor Cells

B Plasma Cells

Antibodies or Immunoglobulins

Complement

Memory B cells

The Bad Guys

Bacteria

Viruses

Fungi

Protozoa (Amoebae)

Helminths

ACT 1

BACTERIA VERSUS THE IMMUNE SYSTEM

Scene One

(Marge is standing at a kitchen table, centre stage, chopping vegetables for a stir-fry dinner with her husband George. We hear a sudden screech and Marge looks shocked...)

MARGE: Ouch! Darn, I've cut myself. Where did I leave those band-aids?

(She exits stage left.)

Scene Two

(The stage is filled with a huge thumb, which we can see both inside and outside. Special microscopic devices allow us to see the characters.)

BACTERIA: Look guys! There's a cut in the skin. Let's go!

(They jump from the knife, table, chopping board and vegetables into the cut.)

NEUTROPHILS *(while patrolling)*: Attention everyone. We just found a cut in the location of left thumb, just above the knuckle. Non-self already present. Prepare for response.

MACROPHAGES: Oh boy, here comes dinner. Yum!

BACTERIA: OK, guys–watch out for the Phil Brothers, especially the neutrophils, and watch out for those macrophage big eaters–those big macs will eat anything including us! Let's get down to business. Get those toxins over here. Let's get down to some serious reproduction!

(Swarms of bacteria start working on the cells, hosing them down with toxins.)

(Stage right, in another part of the body...)

NEUTROPHILS: Attention! Attention! Non-self has been identified as bacteria. We need backup. Calling all neutrophils in the area. Please leave blood stream and report to left thumb immediately!

(Centre stage...)

BACTERIA: Hey, look at this!

BACTERIA: Hey, where'd you get that bit of dead tissue; it's great!

BACTERIA: There's more of it!

BACTERIA: Let's use these pieces of injured tissue to give our toxins more punch. Bacteria are the best; we've got to reproduce!

(Stage right: The neutrophils gather in a huge swarm. A bugle sounds. They run toward the bacteria.)

NEUTROPHILS: Charge! Food! Get your cytoplasm ready, boys! Victory is ours! It's in the bag!!

(They run to the bacteria and begin covering each one with cytoplasm.)

BACTERIA: Look out! It's the old phagocytosis trick. Watch it! They'll try and engulf us! And then they'll eat us!! Look out for those chemicals there!! Ahhhrg!

(Stage left: A large group of backup troops (neutrophils) is lining up for a troop review. We see several of the troops sticking momentarily to capillary walls.)

NEUTROPHILS: Prepare for attack! Prepare to change shape! Get your pseudopods ready! Present...pseudopods! Now remember, guys. These *false feet* will let you enter through any convenient pore of the blood vessel walls.

NEUTROPHIL: Remember, traction is up! We can adhere to the walls of the capillaries when they get sticky!

NEUTROPHILS: It's sticky. Let's go, let's go...

(The army of neutrophils start forward through the blood vessels towards centre stage , the scene of the cut...)

At the scene of the cut.

BACTERIA: Oh no, cytoplasm. Yuck! No!!

BACTERIA: The neutrophils are sending their cytoplasm!!!

BACTERIA: Yuck! Its flowing around us! Help! Help!

BACTERIA: We're trapped!

BACTERIA: In a sac! Help!

BACTERIA: It's the phagosome sacs! Look out! Eeeeeeeeah!

(The neutrophils arrange their pumping equipment everywhere.)

BACTERIA: What's that liquid? What are they doing? Oh no, no, no - here come the enzymes.

BACTERIA: Deadly!

BACTERIA: It's going into the sacs! No! No, no...

BACTERIA: We will be destroyed! Farewell, fellow bacteria!

(A crowd of neutrophils, fat and satisfied-looking, are lumbering to front stage: There they sit or lie, in happy repose.)

NEUTROPHILS: We are getting so full...yum, yum...

NEUTROPHIL: I do feel like I am going to burst. Still, it seems the right way to go. I have done my duty, I am so very full...

NEUTROPHIL: I too am about to burst!

NEUTROPHIL: I am too. Yummmm.

NEUTROPHILS *(in chorus)*: It was a good life. It was a good life.

(Everywhere we see neutrophils bursting in large numbers...)

NEUTROPHIL: I don't feel so sad when I remember that 100 billion of us neutrophils are produced every day. And in a way, I feel destined to burst. It's a neutrophil thing.

NEUTROPHIL: So the loss is normally insignificant.

NEUTROPHIL: Only the good die young. They fought well... farewell...

(The lights dim slowly, but we are able to clearly see as the neutrophils are followed by flank after flank of specialized attackers...)

Scene Three

(Marge and George are seated centre stage at the table, eating salad. Marge is dressed differently, so we know time has passed. They eat in silence for a few moments. Marge finally finishes her salad...)

MARGE: Mmm, that was good.

GEORGE: Sure was. Say, how's your finger?

MARGE *(Looks at band aid and then peels it off)*:   Looks like it never happened! It was itchy and swollen for a while, but it's fine now. Let's watch TV...

George picks up remote control and turns on TV.

TV ANNOUNCER: And in the news tonight, millions of neutrophils lost their lives this week at the scene of a cut in...

MARGE: Wait–let's watch this–looks different!

(Marge and George move to a sofa together, watching the TV, as the lights dim. George, plump and non-athletic, is munching chips and drinking pop.)

ANTIBODY PRODUCTION

B plasma cell

ACT 2

VIRUSES VERSUS THE IMMUNE SYSTEM

Scene One

(As the lights slowly fade up we see a bed at stage right. Marge and George are both asleep. After a few moments, an alarm goes off. George reaches out to shut it off. Gradually he comes to life, gets out of bed, and stretches. Marge is awake, sitting up, and stretching in bed...)

MARGE: How did you sleep, honey?

GEORGE: OK–it just wasn't long enough. Too many late nights, I guess. O, uh, ah, ah, ah, achhooo! *(looks for Kleenex, finds it, blows nose.)*

MARGE: Gesundheit!

GEORGE: I wish I could go back to bed...

Scene Two

(Somewhere in the respiratory tract...)

VIRUS: Hey guys–this body is getting fatigued. This is going to make our job much easier. Wake up, wake up! *(yawns)*

VIRUS: Hey, buddy–guys–over here!

VIRUS: I haven't seen these viruses before. They must have got past the cilia and mucous in order to join us. Hey guys!

VIRUS: Psst–over here. Guys, look at these cells here–they are perfect for you to reproduce in.

VIRUS: Yeah, we had a nap in these cells. They're just what you are looking for.

VIRUS: Yeah, they are just your type. Just look at those juicy cells!

VIRUS: Hey, yeah, let's check it out.

VIRUS: Hey guys, look! These cells are easy to bind with!

VIRUS: Yeah! We are getting that good old chemical reaction. These cells are ours!

VIRUS: It is so easy to get through the outer membrane, and really get to know this cell... *(hums "Getting to know you. . .")*

VIRUS: Oh yeah, this cell is a pushover. We can begin to multiply real soon!

VIRUS: OK. guys. Prepare to take over cell machinery! Pass the word! Pass the word! Prepare for factory mode! We'll start churning out more and more viruses. Let's go!

VIRUS: Isn't it wonderful, being a parasite.

VIRUS: Just like dear old mom and dad...

VIRUS: OK., now we're getting organized.

VIRUS: Yeah, we can use the cell's energy and components. . .

VIRUS: Let's go guys, we'll produce three things: lots and lots of genetic material, viral protein, and viruses...

VIRUS: And produce more viruses!

VIRUS: More virus! More virus! More virus!

NEWLY FORMED VIRUSES: We're ready! Let's bud out on the surface of the cells!

NEW VIRUSES: Bud out! Bud out!

NEW VIRUSES: Lct's go! Let's go! Infect the cells and see them blow!

NEW VIRUSES: More cells, more cells!

NEW VIRUSES: Come on guys, let's burst out!

NEW VIRUSES: And destroy the cell in the process. Such is virus life! Ain't it grand!

NEW VIRUSES: Hurry! Hurry guys, we've got to get to other cells before the macrophages find us.

NEW VIRUSES: Oh! Let's go, let's go, we've got to spread!

NEW VIRUSES: Before the macs eat us up so we are dead!

INFECTED CELLS: Help, help, send for help!

INFECTED CELLS: We are making the protein substance to signal!

INFECTED CELLS: Attention surrounding cells! Virus present, virus present!

INFECTED CELLS: That's it. Slow down the infection!

(As the signals go out, we see a change in the surrounding cells...)

SURROUNDING CELLS: There. That will stop the virus!

SURROUNDING CELLS: You won't get me now!

MACROPHAGES: Attention all macs! Non-self present in the throat. Wakee, wakee, rise-and-shine! Time for breakfast! Prepare to attack!

MACROPHAGES: There they are! Get them! That's it!

MACROPHAGES: Mmm, good, mmm, good!

MACROPHAGES: Yum, yum! Good eats, yeah!

MACROPHAGE: OK. guys: let's chop up the viruses. Get chewing and chopping!

MACROPHAGE: Yeah, and then put pieces of proteins on our surfaces!

MACROPHAGE: Yuck. What for?

MACROPHAGE: Hey buddy, did you forget everything you learned in macrophage school?

MACROPHAGE: Yeah, any macrophage worth it's salt knows why–we've got to signal the T helper cells.

MACROPHAGES: Yeah!

MACROPHAGE: Well, how do we do it?

MACROPHAGE: Just relax, digest, and let it happen naturally...

MACROPHAGES: Man, am I full.

MACROPHAGES: Mmm, me too.

MACROPHAGES: Yeah, urrrp!

MACROPHAGES: Burp!

MACROPHAGES: Burp!

(We see the macrophages spit up tiny bits of virus and display the bits on their surfaces. The bits look something like flags.)

T HELPER CELLS: What do we have here?

T HELPER CELL: Hey guys! The macrophages have the flags out for the good old common cold virus!

T HELPER CELLS: Thanks macrophages. Love it when you guys come through!

T HELPER CELL: Now hear this. Attention T helper cells! We now know that a self cell is infected with an invading virus. This calls for both cellular and humoral immune response!

T HELPER CELL: Red alert! Red alert! Calling all helper T cells. If *you* were programmed in the thymus to recognize the common cold virus, your immune system wants you to reproduce!

T HELPER CELLS: Reporting for duty!

T HELPER CELL: How do we know you were programmed for attack on the cold virus?

T HELPER CELL: Hey, take a look! Why else would these receptors on our surfaces fit? If you'd just take a look at us, you'd see we have the matching pattern of the common cold virus flag that the macrophages are showing. How'd you ever get out of thymus school, buddy?

T HELPER CELL: OK. OK. This is a high pressure situation, just give it a break...

T HELPER CELLS: Come on guys. Let's work together now. We can now lock together with the macrophages with the markers. Let's go! Charge!

(We see a huge number of T helper cells locking into an equally huge number of macrophages...)

MACROPHAGE: Attention! Attention macrophages! It is now time to secrete a hormone which will cause fever in the body. Remember, troops, this will create a hostile environment for the virus. If they can't stand the heat, they will get out of the kitchen!

MACROPHAGE: The hormone also activates the T helper cells! It never fails—it gets them to reproduce at the site of the infection. We need more T helper cells; let's get that hormone pumping!

T HELPER CELL: All right, troops. Listen up here! Remember, we have great responsibility as the captains of the immune system. Remember, we do not actually engage in the destruction of the virus, tempting as that might be. Our job, T helper cells, is sending instructions to all groups of cells engaged in the immune response. Without us, they can't do their jobs.

T HELPER CELL: All right, troops. We've got to get moving. You all know your jobs. We need to begin to secrete various immune system chemicals. The chemicals will call on the rest of the immune system. We'll get this situation under control; let's go!

T HELPER CELLS: Love this heat!

T HELPER CELLS: With this fever we are doing a great job of reproducing ourselves.

T HELPER CELLS: Some of us clones can stay here at the site.

T HELPER CELLS: All right. Let's send others to the spleen and nearest lymph nodes. Move em out!

TRAVELLING T HELPER CELLS: Let's get this hormone message out to the killer T cells that are programmed for the common cold virus. Let's go, troops!

(We see them rush out, stage right...a short time later, they rush in, stage left, and approach a group of T helper cells, and hand them the hormone messages...)

T KILLER CELLS: Thanks for the warning! Now we can grow and reproduce–we'll stop those cold viruses in their tracks!

TRAVELLING T HELPER CELLS: Good to see you guys. We've got to go. We're also going to notify the B cells to begin multiplying with our hormone signals. Bye, and let's move on out!

(We see them rush out, stage right...a short time later, they rush in, stage left, and approach a group of B cells in the blood stream, and hand them the hormone messages...)

B CELL: Attention, B cells! We have just received an official order to change into plasma. Only those of us with receptors for the common cold virus will report for duty. That's it, guys. Let's get that plasma going!

(We see large numbers of B cells transforming into B plasma cells...)

B PLASMA CELL: OK troops. Let's review our job before we start. We can get rid of this cold. Our job is essential–we manufacture antibodies. We're going to take these antibodies, and we're going to neutralize the virus!

B PLASMA CELL: I love making the antibodies! They're just like guided missiles which can only hit this strain of common cold virus. We're going to get those viruses circulating in the fluid; here we come!

B PLASMA CELL: We are mass producing at such a rapid pace that George is feeling fatigue, fever and aches.

B PLASMA CELL: Well, what does George want, anyway? We have to do our job!

(We see the antibodies pouring out of the B plasma area in the fluid...)

RECENTLY MANUFACTURED ANTIBODIES: All right, antibodies! As the new viruses are released into the blood stream from the infected cells, we're ready to pick them off!

RECENTLY MANUFACTURED ANTIBODIES: With the help of complement proteins, in a week, we should be finished our job! The viruses will be overcome! Yeahh!

(We hear cheers from all the immune system cells.)

T KILLER CELLS: We are ready to attack!

T KILLER CELLS: Let's destroy the viruses!

T KILLER CELLS: Let's find those virus-infected cells!

T KILLER CELLS: That flag! There! There's one!

T KILLER CELLS: Let's attach ourselves to it!

T KILLER CELLS: Yeah, puncture the cell's membrane!

T KILLER CELLS: I'm going to inject time-released poisonous granules! Oh boy!

T KILLER CELLS: And that'll blow up the infected cell!

T KILLER CELLS: Before the virus inside has had time to multiply! Yahoo! Let's go! Death to the viruses!

(We see them rush off in search of viruses stage left and right, and all over the stage too. . .)

T HELPER CELLS: What a mess! The wreckage of battle is incredible!

T HELPER CELLS: What we need is more phagocytes!

T HELPER CELLS: Attention, attention! Calling all neutrophils and macrophages in the area. We need your help. Prepare to engulf and destroy the debris of damaged cells and viral material!

NEUTROPHILS: As we give up our lives destroying the debris, George is going to be coughing up a lot of mucous.

NEUTROPHILS: Too bad George doesn't know that mucous means that we immune system cells are winning the battle and he is helping us get rid of the debris.

(As the lights very slowly fade, we see all of the cells we have met, engaged in their various jobs...)

Scene Three

(It is about a week later. As we survey the stage, we see that the viruses are inactivated or destroyed. The stage is much less busy...)

T HELPER CELLS: We need to send another chemical signal to the suppressor T cells.

SUPPRESSOR T CELLS: Attention suppressor T cells! We just received the signal to move in to slow down and stop the immune response. Tell some of the B cells to become memory cells. And tell the others to stop multiplying.

T KILLER CELLS: Our job is done. It is time to stop killing, and disappear. We are getting the message.

SUPPRESSOR T CELLS: Let's get out messages to other T cells and B cells!

SUPPRESSOR T CELLS: Tell them to slow down and eventually halt activity.

SUPPRESSOR T CELLS: Yes, we don't want the immune response to spiral out of control.

MEMORY B CELLS: We need to stay involved, guys. Even though this crisis is past, you never know when the cold virus will try to sneak back. We'll be ready. We'll circulate through the bloodstream and lymphatic system and carry a molecular memory of that particular common cold virus.

MEMORY B CELLS: Yeah, so if that same type of common cold virus should ever reappear, we will be able to get the immune system to swing into action very quickly.

MEMORY B CELLS: Remember guys, we've learned some invaluable lessons from our battles. We'll carry these with us. Though many cells have lost their lives, we remain in George for the rest of his life, primed to respond instantly to that particular common cold virus.

MEMORY B CELLS: The body will never suffer from that particular strain of common cold virus again. If that virus ever shows its face around here, zingo! It'll be gone! We're ready and waiting!

MEMORY B CELLS: Thanks to us, the body is immune to this particular virus after the first bout. Let's hear it for the memory B cells!

(As they cheer, all the cells of the immune system join hands and begin to sway together, cheering this victory over the cold virus. The lights slowly fade on this huge and enthusiastic group who occupy the whole stage, cheering and celebrating...)

ACT 3

FUNGI VERSUS THE IMMUNE SYSTEM

Scene One

(Once again, we see the bedroom. Marge is sitting in front of a mirror, applying make-up. Steam is billowing from the bathroom. The shower sounds stop, and George emerges, clad in a towel. He sits on the edge of the bed...)

MARGE: How did you sleep last night, honey?

GEORGE: Oh, OK. I feel a little better since I finally shook that cold. Maybe those antibiotics the doctor gave me helped, though he said they might not, but they couldn't hurt. I couldn't believe those aches and pains, though. I don't feel that bad now, but I'm still dragging my butt...

MARGE: Maybe we should go to Mexico for a holiday...

Scene Two

(The lights fade down. When they fade up, we see a huge foot, occupying the stage. We can see both the outside and inside of the foot. A group of fungi dance about.)

FUNGI: Come on guys, look at these warm, damp feet. A perfect place to get a good crop of athlete's foot going. Home sweet home, here we come! Hop on, hop on!

(They all rush toward the toes of the foot...)

NEUTROPHILS *(while patrolling)*: Attention, immune system! Non-self present between the third and fourth toes on both feet. Calling for backup!

(Macrophages rush on stage, inside the foot...)

MACROPHAGES: Hmm, they look good. Let's go get 'em!

MACROPHAGE: What do you think? They taste like fungi to me.

MACROPHAGE: Yeah, tastes that way to me too.

FUNGI: We don't need to worry too much about the neutrophils and macrophages.

FUNGI: Yeah, this body has not been looking after itself too well. We have an excellent opportunity to take over!

FUNGI: Let's go, fungi!

NEUTROPHILS: What is taking those backup troops so long? We need more help!

(As we see the fungi growing and taking over the toe areas on the foot, we see that the macrophages are not large in number and have not been able to take on the invaders. We then hear George's voice from off-stage:)

GEORGE: This athlete's foot is really bothering me. I think I had better buy some anti-fungal powder to help me get rid of it. Oh, and I'll pick up some chips, cheesies, and candy to eat while I watch TV tonight. I may be a couch potato, but I get to eat what I want.

(Hours later...)

FUNGI: Oh no, there is powder all over the feet.

FUNGI: And there are no damp areas!

FUNGI: Listen guys, you know George. These feet will probably be warm and damp again in a few days. Let's try again then. Who's for it?

FUNGI: Count me in!

FUNGI: Me too! Let's hear it for the fungi! Yeah!

Scene Three

(We see a portion of the large intestine filling the stage...)

YEAST: I say we attack now, guys. George has been taking antibiotics for a few weeks now.

YEAST: Yeah, the immune system is getting weaker.

YEAST: Yeah, come on, fellow yeast! Now is a great time to take over!

YEAST: We are not called opportunists for nothing! Opportunity knocks, and we respond!

YEASTS: We're the yeast, and we love to feast!

(Meanwhile, nearby...)

NEUTROPHILS: Attention neutrophils. Organize immediately for response to yeast infection.

NEUTROPHILS: We've got to go. I was just over at the intestines and I couldn't find any friendly bacteria at all! The good bacteria in the intestines have been killed off. I'll bet you George has been on antibiotics again.

NEUTROPHILS: Oh, no. The friendly bacteria were good allies. They kept the *Candida Albicans* yeast under control. We've got trouble now!

NEUTROPHILS: OK troops, listen here! With the good bacteria out of commission, we immune system cells won't be able to keep up. We'll just have to do our best under the circumstances.

NEUTROPHILS: We don't want the candida to spread. We have to get things under control again. We need help from the body!

NEUTROPHILS: We hope George will start adding some friendly bacteria into the diet.

NEUTROPHILS: Then we'll get the yeast whipped into shape!

(Nearby...)

YEAST: OK guys, let's just hope George keeps taking antibiotics.

YEAST: Then we will be able to grow and spread throughout the whole body! Nothing can stop us! Yahoo!

YEAST: Remember our game plan, fellow yeasties! Disguises! Build molecules disguised to look like hormone molecules. We can go anywhere!

YEAST: With disguises on the surface, we can enter the body's cellular communication traffic.

YEAST: And we can cause sleepless nights, cramps and all sorts of trouble. Look out George, here we come!

Scene Four

(We are back in the bedroom with George and Marge...)

GEORGE: Mexico? Hey, that's a good idea. I could use a break. I sure didn't sleep well last night. I think I had cramps or something...

MARGE: I'll call the travel agent today.

(The lights fade as Marge hums South of the Border and mimes playing castanets as she does a mock flamenco dance...)

ACT 4

PROTOZOA (AMOEBAE) VERSUS THE IMMUNE SYSTEM

Scene One

(George and Marge are seated at the table in a restaurant in Mexico...)

GEORGE: Well, I've heard this place gets loads of Americans. I guess it should, since they feature delicatessen food, Chinese food, and Mexican food.

MARGE: I guess it'll be safe to eat the lettuce, then...

GEORGE: Yes, you'll probably be OK as long as you avoid the water. Say, is that an iguana over there in the cage? This place is full of surprises. I think I'll try the raw fish and lime juice...

Scene Two

(The stage is filled with enormous lettuce leaves. We can also see protozoa on the lettuce...)

PROTOZOA: I thought we'd never find a host!

PROTOZOA: Patience, amigo. It is lucky we can exist in a dormant state.

PROTOZOA: Yes, as parasitic cysts we can survive for long periods of time outside bodies! Not just any cell can manage that trick. Wait, my friends, we will have our rewards!

PROTOZOA: You're right! It looks like this Marge lady is going for the salad. We'll soon be living high on the hog!

PROTOZOA: Goodbye contaminated soil, water and food; hello Marge!

NEUTROPHILS: Attention everyone, attention! Marge decided they needed a holiday, and we're in the tropics. Be particularly attentive. Remember those protozoa that tried to jump us last time we were here!

PROTOZOA: Whee, I knew this polluted water would get us some place worthwhile.

PROTOZOA: Yeah, down the hatch and into the small intestine!

PROTOZOA: Oh, it's dark in here. That's great! A great place to grow and multiply. A place to flow, a place to grow, proto-proto-proto-zo!

PROTOZOA: Let's head for the large intestine!

PROTOZOA: Yes! We'll penetrate the mucous membranes. There's bacteria galore to feed on there!

NEUTROPHILS: Now hear this! Non-self present in intestines. Get ready to attack!

PROTOZOA: Did you hear that? It is a good thing that we are genetically programmed to alter our surface markers periodically.

PROTOZOA: Yeah, remember last time we had a host? The immune system cells thought they could destroy us, but we altered our markers and disappeared from view! They were lost!

PROTOZOA: We still have to be careful, guys. Another set of immune cells can be programmed to detect our new surface markers. Don't get overconfident.

PROTOZOA: Relax, buddy. We can just alter our markers and disappear from view. It works every time! We can do it as many times as we need to. We're all set!

NEUTROPHILS: Attention, attention neutrophils! Non-self has been identified as protozoa. We need backup!

NEUTROPHIL: Calling all neutrophils in the area. Please leave blood stream and report to intestines!

NEUTROPHIL: That's it, guys, over here. Keep on coming, that's it! We've got to keep this population of intestinal parasites under control!

NEUTROPHIL: OK, guys. We've got to communicate with other parts of the body. If we're lucky, maybe we can create some diarrhea.

NEUTROPHIL: That will help some of the protozoa cysts pass out of the body before they can break open. Getting rid of those parasites will make our job easier.

Scene Three

(We see Marge, head propped up on pillow, lying in bed in a Mexican hotel room. George is sitting by a table filled with glasses and liquids, reading a newspaper...)

MARGE: Some holiday this was, George. It's all I can do to keep ginger ale down. I can't drink the water. I feel just awful. Oh, oh, it's time to visit the bathroom again. I hope I can stand the flight back.

GEORGE: A week of Montezuma's revenge, as they call this bug you have, is too much. Let's fly home tomorrow.

(George helps Marge stagger towards the bathroom door.)

Scene Four

(Inside Marge's body...)

NEUTROPHIL: Well, troops, it has taken two weeks, but we're back in control. Remember, we can't get all those pesky protozoa, they're always putting on new disguises.

MACROPHAGE: At least we've got enough of them killed off that Marge will be OK. I'm as sick of eating protozoa as she is of staring at bathroom walls!

NEUTROPHIL: OK, guys, the T suppressor cells have told us to wind down the immune system response. You all know the drill! Say goodbye to our dead troops! Time to move on out. Let's look for new challenges!

Scene Five

(Marge is in the living room, on the telephone...)

MARGE: Yes, I'm fine now, but I thought I'd lose my insides for a while...I guess it was some lettuce I ate...yes, I'm fine now, but I was in bed a week. Yes, and weak and feeble! I couldn't believe how awful I felt... OK, talk to you later.

(Hangs up telephone.)

MARGE: I can't believe how good it feels to be home again! George, George?

GEORGE *(from off-stage)*: Yes, dear?

MARGE: Could you be sure to pick up some salad greens for dinner when you're shopping?

GEORGE: Sure thing, dear.

ACT 5

HELMINTHS VERSUS THE IMMUNE SYSTEM

Scene One

(George is shopping in a fish market, and chatting with the owner.)

GEORGE: Yeah, it was lovely, right by the ocean. But Marge got sick with Montezuma's revenge as they call it. By the way, I had a great fish dish, when I was down there.

OWNER: What was it?

GEORGE: Some kind of raw fish and lime juice. Say, what have you got that's fresh? I seem to be hungry all the time.

OWNER: How do you like this salmon—it's fresh this morning...

Scene Two

(We see a portion of the stomach filling the stage...)

PARASITIC WORM: You may have liked that fish George—so did we. We love to live in undercooked meat, fish and snails.

PARASITIC WORM: And we love to live inside the human body and feed off the body's nutrients. Right, George?

NEUTROPHILS *(while patrolling)*: Attention. Attention! Non-self present in the stomach!

MACROPHAGES: Yum. Looks good.

MACROPHAGES: I think it tastes like tapeworm.

MACROPHAGES: I'm not sure. I can't quite get through. Let's show the T cells the little bit we were able to get, though.

PARASITIC WORM: Oh, oh. Here come the T cells. Remember, worms, we have a thick, waxy protective coating to protect us from these guys. They won't even recognize us!

PARASITIC WORM: Yeah, the coating makes it difficult for the immune system to penetrate us.

PARASITIC WORM: We can masquerade as body cells. We should be able to fool them!

PARASITIC WORM: We can trick the body into thinking we are self cells.

PARASITIC WORM: Fellow worms, you are safe with us! Just gather substances shed from surfaces of real body cells and drape them around our outer membranes! Quickly, now, I can hear the T cells coming!

T CELLS: What the heck gives here, macrophages?

T CELLS: We thought you said there were tapeworms here. All we can see are self markers.

MACROPHAGES: You know those parasitic worms. They're a bunch of worms! They're always sneaking around, pretending to be self. Don't blame us!

MACROPHAGES: We were able see what their original markers looked like, so we'll be on the lookout for new, undisguised tapeworms.

T CELLS: OK, call if you find any you can get your teeth into! Good luck.

PARASITIC WORM: Caution will help us survive, fellow worms. Remember—it's essential that the T cells and antibodies don't find our mouths.

PARASITIC WORM: Yes, our Achilles heel is our mouth! It is our only unprotected area. If they find your mouth, they'll get you, so try and avoid them!

PARASITIC WORM: And remember too—as long as the body stays out of balance, we can exist here for as long as we want. We just need to be careful not to eat too much, so the body can survive.

PARASITIC WORM: We don't want the body to die. If it does, we will have to find a new home. So go easy.

Scene Three

(George and Marge are seated on the sofa...)

GEORGE: Marge, I'm going to see my doctor. First it was that miserable cold, and then the athlete's foot really plagued me. Now I still don't feel just right. Maybe I need to change my lifestyle.

MARGE: George, my little couch potato, what's happened to you!

GEORGE: I just want to feel good. Maybe there's more to life than junk food and TV.

MARGE: George, it sounds like you've discovered the importance of enhancing wellness! I'm thrilled!

GEORGE: Maybe, Marge, maybe. We'll see, we'll see.

(As they move slowly closer to each other to embrace, the curtain descends...)

The End.

Chapter 7

MORE ENEMIES OF THE IMMUNE SYSTEM

I llness or disease often is the immune system saying it's *out of balance*. When we are out of balance we unknowingly invite disease by handicapping or destroying our natural defenses.

This chapter will deal with the stressors that create imbalance in the body. There are some things we can avoid (or try to), such as the chemical stressors in our diet and environment. We can also learn to adapt to stress in general. What we want is the *right* kind of stress, for the *right* length of time, at the *right* level for our individual bodies in order to support the immune system.

Stress In Lifestyle

What is stress? Dr. Hans Selye defined stress as the nonspecific response of the body to any demand made upon it. If stress is the body's reaction to any demand placed upon it, then stress is either positive or negative. We place a demand on the body simply by standing, walking, or talking. Virtually all human activity involves stress. The stress response is essential; without it we would not live long. When there are no demands placed upon us, we are dead.

A factor or situation that produces stress is a stressor. A stressor is any stimulus, internal or external, which causes a change in our functioning or behaviour. Anything that requires some readjustment or adaptation can be a stressor. Since circumstances and the environment are always changing, we are always under some stress.

Stressors can take many forms. They may be physical (structural, nutritional, chemical or environmental), mental, emotional, or spiritual. If we can stop, get away or release the tension after a stress reaction, then there is no stress build up. But when stress is excessive, constant and we can't stop or get away from the cause, or can't find a way to release the tension then there is distress. Our ability to adapt is further jeopardized by such factors as age or genetic weakness. When stressors come from more than one area, for example structural, chemical and emotional, then the body has less of a chance to adapt. Stress factors are cumulative and as soon as the body's threshold is reached, we will experience distress.

Everyone has their own unique response to distress. Responses can be physical, i.e. headaches, adrenal exhaustion, muscle tension, digestive problems, or fatigue. In addition, responses may be emotional, such as anxiety, depression, or fear. Behavioural responses may be overeating, cigarette smoking, or interpersonal conflicts. Distress responses may also be psychological, such as insecurity, indecision, or self-rejecting thoughts like "I'm no good." There is a direct causal relationship between what you think and the way you feel: "I feel overwhelmed and hopeless", may make you feel, "My disease must be impossible to resolve." These responses or symptoms invite us to investigate our feelings, attitudes, self talk, belief systems, and our lifestyle.

In human conflict, we can stay all keyed up without ever resolving our difficulties with each other. When we get uptight about something that is perceived as a stressor, instead of acting out the bodily instinct, we hold back and let it act on us. The standoff is probably more harmful to your health than an occasional straightforward and honest verbal battle. This pattern probably contributes as much to our poor health as does inadequate nutrition.

In chapter two, we saw that chronic stress can inhibit the functioning of the immune system. The American Medical Association reports that nearly 80% of diseases are either stress-related, or stress antagonized. North American businesses lose an estimated $100 billion annually because of premature deaths and health-related absenteeism due to poorly managed stress.

As long ago as 1937, Canada's famous stress expert, Dr. Hans Selye, reported that stress brought about a drop in the number of lymphocytes in the blood. Other scientific studies indicate that natural killer cells and phagocytes may also be impaired. High levels of stress cause the adrenal gland (a part of endocrine system related to the fight or flight response) to release increased amounts of cortisol (a potent steroid). This steroid has the ability to suppress immune and inflammatory responses. Cortisol-like steroids are used routinely on transplant patients (to prevent the immune system from rejecting the non-self transplant organ) and in the treatment of autoimmune diseases.

Mental and Emotional Stressors

Our mind may be the most powerful source of stress. Our minds first have to perceive the situation or event as a stressor, or some sort of threat. Then our past experiences govern our expectations of how well we can cope with the situation. If we expect that we can't cope with the stressor, then we have expectations of the consequences and that further increases our level of stress. Our interpretation of the facts determines our thoughts. Thoughts can create or add to stress.

When we feel helpless, overwhelmed, threatened, uncertain or not in control, we feel stress. As children we often felt helpless and many times decisions were made for us. We did not feel in control. In times of stress as adults, we sometimes resort to feeling how we did when we were children. Stress in our minds is based on a perceived threat and at a fundamental level always evokes the emotion fear. Change can also be a perceived threat as it calls upon us to adapt. Any adaptation stresses us, especially if we feel it will endanger our survival.

Every time we feel threatened or challenged and we cannot figure out some constructive ways to handle our feelings, our bodies prepare for battle. Stressors such as deadlines are only as bad as you let your mind make them. Stress is not someone being angry with you–it's how your mind (your perception based on your belief system) interprets such an event.

For example, your boss comes to you and gives you an urgent task with a specific deadline. You can say to yourself, "There is no way I can do this." Your body is responding to the task as a stressor. Or, you can say, "I'll do the best I can". When faced with such a situation, step back and look on it as something you can deal with (control) and make the best of it. Use your energy to improve things, not worry about them. Have a positive optimistic outlook.

Remember what may stress one person may not affect another. Dr. Hans Selye thinks that the most frequent causes of distress are psychological–that is to say, lack of adaptability. When we choose our responses we are in control of stress.

Managing stress requires a sense of being in control of our lives; having different choices or responses to the same stimulus. Drs. Singer and Glass bombarded two groups of working subjects with identical noise. One group had the option of pressing a button if the noise became too bothersome, to stop it. The other group did not. Most of the people in the first group completed their work without pressing the button. Yet the two groups of people showed startling differences in their ability to do all sorts of tasks after the noise was over. Those people without the button made errors on reading tasks and arithmetic problems, showed little tolerance for frustration and were unwilling to do favours for other people. The people who had access to the button, showed almost none of these after-effects. They had a feeling of control.

Mental stress, both moderate and severe, can affect the workings of our white blood cells. In one study, Drs. Janice Kiecolt-Glaser and Ronald Glaser at the Ohio State University College of Medicine demonstrated that the lymphocytes found in the blood of hospitalized psychiatric patients suffering se-

vere depression underwent a slower self-repair process than those found in the patients not suffering from such a mental disorder. The investigators reported that their laboratory study was evidence that depression can be associated with an increased risk of cancer and infectious disease.

Another study showed that the suffering of a widower over the loss of his wife may harm his health: Bereavement seems to prevent lymphocytes from reacting appropriately. Even the much milder strain of taking an exam appears to reduce T cell activity. On the other hand, steps as simple as regular moderate exercise, or learning to identify and change the negative thinking which accompanies depression have been shown to reduce depression in controlled research. Positive attitudes may enhance the immune system and challenge disease.

Emotions can negatively affect our bodies. Emotions held in the mind and repressed, will eventually show up in the physical body. A study at the University of Michigan's School of Public Health showed that if people with high blood pressure keep anger inside, they increase the risk of premature death five times.

We need to learn to adapt, to feel in control and know that we have choices as adults. Managing stress is in fact managing the mind or our perception of external events. Our internal dialogue or self talk and our self image needs to change so we feel good about ourselves and our thoughts. We need to determine how realistic the stressor is; not underrate our ability to cope. We can challenge underlying irrational belief systems and get in touch with our feelings. On a behaviourial level, we need to be more assertive, and learn how to communicate better. We can be open to listening and acknowledging others, find solutions to problems, stop avoiding or escaping trivial stressors, and reward our own successes. On a physical level, we need to increase our endurance capacity through exercise, look after our bodies and learn to relax. (See the next chapter for more specific ideas.)

The body is a series of complex systems, each interacting with the other. The mind is the master of all these systems, operating the units of its command by releasing certain hormones and by sending electrical impulses through the nervous, endocrine and immune systems network. Obviously, undue stress can seriously affect the body's immune system.

Physical Stressors:

Structural, Nutritional, Chemical, Environmental

Structural Stressors

Distress can cause tension in the muscles. When muscles are tight or in spasm, they contract and cause pain. When muscles in our necks or backs are contracted they pull on the vertebrae in our spinal column. Our spine houses part of our nervous system, so when the muscles tighten up, a vertebrae can become displaced. The result may be a pinched nerve. This causes pain in the area controlled by the nerve. If there are organs controlled by the affected nerve, there may be discomfort or malfunction of these organs.

Even the slightest displacement of a vertebrae can produce pressure or irritation upon the nerves. This affects the communication of the vital nerve impulses to the organs, cells and tissues of the body. Our nervous system controls and monitors all body parts and functions. It controls the communication both within the body and between the body and its surroundings. We know there is a connection between the nervous system and the immune system, so it is important to look after structural stressors. Find out what stressors are causing your muscles to tighten up.

Nutritional And Chemical Stressors

We stress our bodies when we ask them to assimilate toxic substances that do damage or are impossible to absorb.

Scientists at the University of California in San Francisco have found that alcohol, besides killing liver macrophages, causes liver cells to attract white blood cells. The liver is your body's detoxification centre. Doctors already knew that large numbers of immune cells could be found in damaged and inflamed livers of people who drank heavily. But now they see something new. The evidence indicates that liver cells, as soon as they have absorbed alcohol, send out a message that calls in the defense troops; these defending white cells actually do the damage, attacking the liver. This means alcohol may set off a kind of autoimmune disease in the liver—a disease in which the immune system attacks the self cells of the body.

Macrophage

Cigarette smoking has many impacts on immune cells. A U.S. Surgeon General's report summed up a number of studies indicating an impairment of immune responses in smokers. Lung macrophages in these people were less able to carry out their normal functions. Another study indicated a component of cigarette smoke, nitrogen oxide, reduces resistance to viral infections, possibly by lessening the production of interferon (a protein which inhibits viral growth). Other studies reported that smoking lessens production of antibodies, and that smokers are more susceptible during outbreaks of influenza. Cigarette smoke can also overload and paralyse the small hairs - cilia - that line the air passages. The natural air-filtering system is then unable to stop bacteria and parasites from entering the lungs. Habitual smoking can lead to a complete loss of this natural defense system. Researchers also found that components of cigarette smoke reduced the number of B cells in the spleen.

The number one cause of lung cancer is smoking. Smokers increase their risk of stroke 20%. Absenteeism rates are one-third to one-half higher for smokers than nonsmokers. Smoking can increase risk of miscarriage or stillbirth by about 50%. Cigarettes have sugar added to them during the curing process to hide the bitter taste of tobacco. Cigarettes not only contain addictive substances, they also rob the body of vitamin C.

Another aspect of smoking is second-hand smoke. Two-thirds of the smoke from a burning cigarette goes into the environment. This smoke has twice the nicotine, five times the carbon monoxide, and fifty times the ammonia than smoke that is directly inhaled.

Refined white sugar is devitalized, demineralized and robbed of any life giving qualities. It is empty calories with no nutritional value. While sugar is being absorbed into the body, you may feel a quick pick-up as the adrenals are gathering every resource to deal with the sugar. The adrenals are concerned with keeping blood sugar levels up in the body. The pancreas is concerned with keeping blood sugar levels down. This causes stress in the body. The glucose levels drop and you feel listless and tired or jumpy. Wanting another lift, most people eat more sugar. The adrenals end up worn out and eventually become damaged. Sugar also robs the body of vitamins, especially vitamins C and B. Excessive use of sugar is one of the causes of diabetes and hypoglycemia. Sugar in the diet can cause weight gain. Sugar itself is a stressor to the immune system, because as we saw in chapter two, the endocrine system (adrenals and pancreas) and immune system communicate back and forth.

Caffeine in coffee, black teas, colas and chocolate may deprive the immune system of the sleep period required for rebuilding the immune supplies. It also impairs the nervous system by opposing the action of a neurotransmitter. Neurotransmitters are chemicals released from nerve endings. This suppression of a neurotransmitter may affect communication to, from, or within the immune system. Remember that the immune system and nervous system work together.

One cup of coffee causes stomach acid secretion increases. Over a period of time this can cause serious stomach disorders. Your heart speeds up. In response, the principle brain centre for slowing the heart is activated. This creates tension which can lead to arrhythmia and irregularity of heart action. Your lungs work harder, blood vessels in your brain get narrower, and your overall metabolism goes up 15 to 25%. The kidneys have to work harder.

Caffeine also triggers adrenal hormones (associated with fight or flight) into action, which cause an initial lift and increased sense of well-being, mental clarity and alertness. Since caffeine has no food value, this extra surge of energy must come from your body's emergency reserve system. This action can depress the immune system. Also, when adrenalin

T suppressor

is added to the blood it raises the cholesterol levels. Coffee drinkers increase their risk of heart disease by 35% over non-coffee drinkers.

Street drugs affect the brain. The brain's response to the drugs affects the immune system. Research shows street drugs reduce the number of T cells, inhibit antibody formation, and impair normal functioning of the immune system.

Researchers have learned that certain people sometimes experience marked changes in the immune system when they eat particular foods. Sugar, milk, wheat, corn, peanuts and chocolate bring about mood changes, making them irritable, anxious, or depressed, even though they may not have allergic reactions to them. In a University of Chicago study, 16 of 23 subjects with measurable mood changes resulting from foods had significantly lower levels of complement (the family of proteins that act with antibodies to kill invaders) in their blood. The unpleasant emotions such people feel may be a message from their immune cells trying to tell them a particular food isn't doing the cells any good. Brain chemicals that modify moods can affect immune cells.

Artificial colourings, flavourings, preservatives, additives, pesticide residues, traces of fertilizers and toxic heavy metals (which provide no nourishment) create an overload of toxins for the body to eliminate. They can interfere with biochemical reactions and enzymatic processes which weaken the immune system. For example, in countries where smoked foods are commonly consumed, cancer rates are higher.

Overfeeding the body reduces its ability to fight off infections, according to the University of Toronto's Dr. Bernhard Cinader. He says that restricting calories fed to mice makes their immune systems more effective. But, he adds, genetic differences between strains of mice or between individuals, play a key part in the way diet affects the immune system.

We have some control over whether we put these damaging substance in our bodies or not. We also have some control over whether we overeat. But sometimes that is easier said than done. We are only human, after all. In some situations our negative self-talk about self denial ("I look like a fat cow so I better not eat that") may do worse damage, through the body/mind connection, to the immune system than the substances themselves. There is a direct causal relationship between what you think and the way you feel.

At other times the addictions take over. Even though we know it is not good for our immune systems, that taste sensation of chocolate is all we want. What are our bodies saying to us with these addictions? There are many theories and I would like to suggest one of them that may be helpful in trying to understand such cravings.

We eat for many different reasons, the main reasons being emotional, nutritional (to provide our bodies with the vital fuel), or because it's breakfast, lunch or dinnertime. There is a lot of confusion between food and feelings. Many of us use food to cover up emotions. We eat when we are sad, angry, bored or feeling empty inside. This confusion began when we were infants. Being held by our mothers while being fed, allowed us to associate food with love or reward. So for most of us food being associated with feelings began very early. As adults, many of us continue this association and we eat to avoid unpleasant feelings. Unfortunately many of us are not even aware of this. We are aware only of the craving. The sad part is that overeating or eating something with no nutritional value pacifies for the moment; a temporary reward.

Dealing with our emotional difficulties will make controlling our addictive behaviours easier to do. Getting our emotional needs met comes from our interaction with people or feeling fulfilled in life. For instance, if you have cravings for sugar, ask yourself, "Do I have enough sweetness in my life?" Another helpful question we can ask ourselves before we put food in our mouths is: "What nutritional value does this food have?". We need to learn to separate feelings and food and realize that they are different. Food gives us nutrition which gives us energy. Make sure the proportion of nutritional food outweighs the emotional food.

It is clear that addictive behaviours such as excessive drinking, smoking, or eating, etc., can harm immune functioning. To support our immune systems, we need to be careful not to put any additional stress on our systems and to choose foods high in nutritional value.

Bacteria

Environmental Stressors

More and more people are succumbing to environmental stresses, the result of ever increasing environmental pollution.

Our environment (food, water, air, clothes, cars, offices and home) is saturated with chemicals, many potentially dangerous to our health. Pesticides, solvents, lead, mercury, chloroform, DDT, DDE, and asbestos are chemicals that invite disease by handicapping or destroying our immune system.

Among people with environment-induced hypersensitivity, only five in 100 suffer the severe total syndrome. Many have mild effects. For a number of them, exposure to offending substances occurs in the workplace. Modern-day sealed office buildings, with faulty ventilation in windowless, air-conditioned towers can cause a host of unwanted reactions. The air in such enclosed spaces can build up high concentrations of pollutants. This, coupled with an increase in synthetic fibres, scented items, cleaning supplies, pesticides, gas appliances and heaters, inadequate cleaning of carpets, fumes from building materials or business machines, lead to what is called the *sick-building syndrome*.

Investigations of two situations in Japan and Taiwan found that people exposed to high levels of industrial chemicals for a substantial amount of time displayed a variety of changes in their antibodies and helper T cells. It is important to go to doctors who are familiar with these health hazards, so that the diagnosis includes effects on the nervous system, the endocrine system, and the immune system.

A dentistry professor at the University of Southern California, has found the immune system can be adversely affected by mercury. His early studies showed a reduction of T cells in patients with amalgam fillings that contain mercury. The

ANTIBODY PRODUCTION

B plasma cell

American Dental Association estimates that fewer than one per cent of people are hypersensitive to mercury.

Mark Friedlander and Terry Phillips in their book, *Winning the War Within*, suggest toxic substances are also potential immune system enemies:

"Toxic substances, although not live invaders, can ultimately do just as much damage as the others. Heavy metal contaminants and air, water and food pollutants do not actually stimulate the immune system into attack. Rather, they kill those cells that they come into contact with by direct chemical reaction. In most cases, the poisonous chemical suffocates the cells by destroying the enzymes required by the cell for life support. Without the enzyme, the cell dies. The disastrous effects upon the body are then direct. But the effect on the immune system is indirect. The debris of these suffocated cells circulating in the rivers of the blood and lymph systems can trigger the production of auto-antibodies—antibodies that respond to the dead cells as if they were foreign. This can ultimately lead to autoimmune diseases or to cancer."

As one environmentalist said, "Man has treated the environment harshly for so many years that it is now striking back". Some researchers have suggested that people with immune system diseases are like the canaries that miners once kept below ground as an early warning of hazardous conditions. If the birds became sick or died, the miners knew the air in the mine was impure. Some doctors say society should be heeding the warning being given by the most sensitive of humans among us.

Summary

This chapter has introduced you to some of the basic enemies of good immune system functioning. The list is not complete, but with this elementary knowledge, you may be able to avoid some of the enemies of the immune system. By avoiding these more obvious physical, mental and emotional stressors you will help to improve your immune system functioning so it can deal with the other more invisible enemies. In the next chapter, we will deal with such practices as meditation, relaxation, and visualization to help with stressors. They can't prevent you from encountering stressful events but they can reduce the distress of stress—and improve health.

Chapter 8

FRIENDS OF THE IMMUNE SYSTEM

There are many different ways to strengthen the immune system. Diet, clean air, breathing, exercise, sleep, meditation, relaxation and creating a network of friends are some basics. Being healthy mentally, emotionally and spiritually, and working with visualization are also important ways to keep your immune system strong. All of these friends of the immune system influence us at the physical, mental, emotional and spiritual levels. These levels are all related and interdependent on each other. Diet, for example, can affect the physical level directly, but it will also affect the other three levels in more subtle ways.

Diet/nutrition

There is an increasing body of information that shows that your immune system relies on your diet to a large extent for its health. The care and feeding of your immune system calls for common sense. You need a wide variety of natural foods to nourish your body. There is little doubt that a poor diet weakens immune responses. Good diet is essential, because what you eat provides building blocks for the body to build white blood cells and antibodies. If you don't give your body defenses the nutrients they need to do their jobs, invaders that gain entry to the body might meet with little resistance.

The human body is approximately 65 - 70 per cent water. Water is contained in blood vessels, inside cells and surrounding cells. It is vital to our existence. We can survive many weeks without food but only a few days without water. It is important for our electrolyte (mineral) balance. Water transports molecules of salt, potassium and nutrients into cells, and allows waste materials to exit. Water also helps regulate body temperature; it cools the body as it evaporates when we sweat. Water provides lubrication for the movement of our joints. Water is also important for the digestive process. We need to drink good clean water every day. Water purification may be important in the area you live. We need to be aware that coffee, tea, fruit juice, milk and other liquids are processed as food and the body needs water. We would not put coffee in our car battery instead of water, so we need to treat our bodies with the same respect.

Because water is so vital for our bodies, it is important to eat water-rich foods. To enhance the immune system, fruits, vegetables, cooked grains and beans need to be the predominant types of food (at least 70% of our daily intake). Fresh vegetables and fruit are more nutritious than frozen, and frozen is better than canned. The more the food is processed the less nutrient value it has.

Vitamins and minerals are the keys that unlock the potential of three major nutrients - proteins, carbohydrates and fats (lipids). Vitamins are organic compounds required for normal growth and are essential for life. With a few exceptions, the body cannot synthesize vitamins; they must be supplied in the diet or in dietary supplements. They are necessary for converting food into energy or into cell tissues. They function with chemicals called enzymes. Vitamins aid in the enzyme activity of the digestive process. They are the key ingredient in manufacturing hormones in the endocrine system. Vitamins also affect the vital functioning of organs as well as the immune system.

All the vitamins are necessary for a healthy body. However, results of studies reported by the World Health Organization (WHO) show that some of the vitamins have a powerful effect on immune cells.

- Vitamin A helps prevent damage within cells caused by so-called free radicals. Free radicals are compounds which have an abnormal (unpaired) number of atoms, so they are highly reactive and can bash around inside the cells. Vitamin A, along with vitamins C and E, sponge them up.

- B vitamins affect the production of antibodies.

- Vitamin C can increase production of interferon, one of the good substances cells make when they are infected with viruses.

- Vitamin C also helps preserve the thymus and other lymph organs and increases the power of macrophages to engulf and chew up bacteria.

- Vitamin C helps protect against damage from free radicals.

- Vitamin E plays a role in wound healing, reducing inflammation and also protects against damage from free radicals.

- Vitamin E increases the proliferation of antibody-producing B cells. B cells shift production of antibodies from IgM to IgG, a more effective type of antibody.

- Vitamin E seems to enhance co-operation between T helper cells and B cells.

- Vitamin E increases the effectiveness of macrophages in chewing up bacteria.

Minerals are nutrients that exist in the body and in food in organic and inorganic combinations. Minerals, like vitamins, act as catalysts for many biological reactions in the body. They are important in the production of hormones and help control the water balance inside us. They also maintain acid/alkaline balance and aid in the creation of antibodies. Minerals need to be supplied in the diet.

All minerals, in the correct balance, are needed for a healthy body, but several minerals appear to be essential to the immune system.

- Zinc appears to be the most important for maintaining immune integrity. A shortage of zinc causes a shrinkage of the thymus gland, which in turn causes a loss of T cells of all kinds.

- Copper is needed by the thymus gland to produce its hormones.

- Selenium, working in concert with vitamin E, improves production of antibodies.

- Iron is an ingredient in chemicals made by T cells.

Each of us is biochemically unique. We all have different metabolisms and therefore different nutritional requirements. There are as many different diets as there are people. You may need to consult a nutritional consultant or your doctor to see what your individual body needs. I will give some suggested daily intakes of minerals and vitamins. Keep in mind that there is no such thing as a single deficiency. Vitamins and minerals have a complex interrelationship, so if you take supplements without consulting a professional, use the total broad spectrum method of supplementation. The immune system itself always responds to a mineral imbalance, as it does to a vitamin imbalance. Without the correct intake, protein production is inhibited and the production of antibodies is reduced.

Suggested Daily Doses (Minimum - Maximum)

       Vitamin A - 25,000 - 75,000 I.U.
       Vitamin D - 650 - 1,300 I.U.
       Vitamin E - 400 - 900 I.U.
       Vitamin C - 1,000 - 6,000 mg.
       Vitamin B-1 - 25 - 250 mg.
       Vitamin B-2 - 25 - 150 mg.
       Vitamin B-6 - 60 - 250 mg.
       Vitamin B-12 - 100 - 2,000 mcg.
       Niacin, Niacinamide - 25 - 150 mg.
       Pantothenic Acid - 100 - 1,500 mg.
       Folic Acid - 0.4 - 2 mg.
       Biotin - 25 - 250 mcg.
       Choline - 50 - 2,000 mg.
       Inositol - 25 - 500 mg.
       P.A.B.A. - 16 - 500 mg.
       Calcium - 400 - 1,000 mg.
       Magnesium - 350 - 800 mg.

Potassium - 100 - 1,000 mg.
Iron - 10 - 20 mg.
Zinc - 15 - 100 mg.
Iodine - 0.125 - 0.5 mg.
Copper - 0.25 - 2 mg.
Chromium - 150 - 250 mcg.
Manganese - 5 - 20 mg.
Selenium - 150 - 300 mcg.

Proteins are an essential component in building cells and supplying hormones and enzymes. Next to water, protein is the most plentiful substance in the body. Adequate protein in the diet is essential for the production of antibodies. Excess protein is often stored in the body as fat.

Fats are essential to a balanced diet, as are proteins and carbohydrates, but only in correct proportions. For most adults fat needs to be under 30% of the total caloric intake. Fats (lipids) are the most concentrated source of energy in the diet. Fat can be stored for emergency energy needs so the body won't take from the protein supply. Fats help absorb and transport fat-soluble vitamins (A,D,E,and K). They regulate many of the hormones including the prostaglandins, which control macrophages and neutrophils. They are also important in the production of steroids, one of the chemical regulators of the immune system.

Macrophage

The human body cannot make all fatty acids, and must get the essential fatty acids from food. In one study, people deprived of essential fatty acids produced an abnormal number of antibodies. Such people also had an imbalance of T cells, with a significant loss of suppressor cells. A similar imbalance is frequently seen in autoimmune diseases.

In general, diet in North America is too heavy in fats. Such a diet, by its effects on the thymus gland, leads to a shortage of effective T cells.

Carbohydrates are the chief source of energy for all body functions and muscular exertion. They are necessary to assist in the digestion and assimilation of other foods. They help regulate protein and fat metabolism.

Simple carbohydrates are sugars. They can be refined (e.g. table sugar, corn syrup, molasses, etc.) or they can be unrefined (e.g. fruit). Complex carbohydrates are starches. They can be refined (e.g. bread, pasta, crackers, cake, white rice, etc.), or they can be unrefined (e.g. vegetables, beans, whole grains, etc.). Unrefined complex carbohydrates provide fibre, and take longer to be broken down into simple sugars so they sustain you longer. In combination with proteins, carbohydrates form substances that are essential to immune system functioning. A high-fibre diet has been shown to reduce the rate of colon and rectal cancers.

There is much controversy around the connection between disease processes and diet. Some centres claim that certain foods make symptoms of disease worse and that when patients fast and follow special diets, their immune systems become more balanced and their disease abates. Others dismiss the claims. As scientists weed out facts, they find changed food patterns a possible explanation for the improvement in some select patients with certain diseases. The best person to test these claims is yourself, in consultation with a doctor sympathetic to the possibility that you can reduce disease symptoms through diet.

As a Nutritional Consultant I have worked with many clients who have balanced out their immune systems using diet. The clients who have incorporated the diet changes into their lifestyles are still disease free today. They also made other lifestyle changes as well.

Bacteria

Another aspect of nutrition is the use of herbs. Herbs have functioned both as food and medicine for centuries. Like vitamins and minerals, herbs perform certain functions in the body. Some herbs work with the body to fight infections. Herbs help the body with the cleansing and eliminating process. Certain herbs also help strengthen and normalize glands, nourish the body and stimulate energy levels within the body.

Some research done at the M.B. Anderson hospital at the University of Texas reported that Chinese herbs strengthen the immune system. In this research, they took cancer patients, measured their immune strength, compared them to normal peoples' immune strength and found that cancer patients' immune strength was much declined. They then gave them Chinese herbs, measured their immune strength and found that in 90 per cent of the patients the immune strength went from below normal to above normal.

There is much more I could say on the subject of nutrition as it has filled volumes. This is a very simplified overview keeping the immune system as the focus. In a world of processed foods, it is important to eat as many raw, organic, water-rich and unprocessed foods as possible. Eat a variety of foods as well. If processed foods are in your diet, then it is important to take vitamin and mineral supplements to support your immune system.

Air and Breathing

Your immune system needs clean air, as oxygen is another compound on which your body is dependent. We cannot live very long without it. Oxygen is supplied via the blood to all the cells in the body.

Learning to change shallow breathing into deep breathing is another aid to your immune system. Cells need oxygen to break down carbohydrates and fats in order to obtain energy. Breathing has to convey oxygen from the atmosphere to the blood cells, and carry the unwanted carbon dioxide back to the atmosphere. Breath is essential to healing. Deep breathing helps move your lymph, and your lymph moves the toxins out of the body. By increasing general vitality, breathing increases the power of your immune system.

When outdoors, spend as much time as you can away from major metropolitan centres, industrial areas or highways. Take some time to be at the beach, in the mountains or in the country where there are lots of trees and the air smells so great that you notice it helps you sleep at night.

When indoors, increase your ventilation by opening windows. If that isn't possible, use an air purifier. Cut down on products that pollute, such as anything synthetic, pesticides, scented products, products containing formaldehyde, and avoid smoking. House plants, such as spider plants have been found by NASA to substantially reduce the trace chemicals emitted by so many marvels of modern chemistry.

Exercise

Regular exercise is important for immune system health. The physical body benefits from exercise because the lymph needs muscular movement in order to flow. Healthy circulation is essential, because the blood and lymph vessels are the main pathways for antibodies. These vessels transport antibodies to the sites of infection and diseases. Exercise raises the body temperature slightly for short periods. This creates an excellent environment for the immune system to do its job. For example, studies show that exercise keeps the bloodstream flowing and raises the levels of T cells. Exercise also insures body tone, reducing the cellular breakdown that begins the aging process. This breakdown often introduces the onset of autoimmune diseases (where the immune system attacks the self cells).

One of the best exercises is brisk walking. It is a good low impact exercise for general health, and it benefits all parts of the body. When you walk with your arms swinging, it balances the brain hemisphere co-operation.

Another excellent exercise is rebounding. Rebounding is jumping on a piece of equipment that looks like a small trampoline. It is different from other forms of exercise because it puts gravity to work for you with the least amount of muscular effort. The bouncing action of the rebounder stimulates the lymphatic system to function more effectively.

Aerobic exercise increases the fitness of your heart and lungs, helping to prevent heart disease and directly increasing your physical endurance. When you are fit, your body can cope with increased levels of stress without overloading it. Exercise creates flexibility. This is important because when we have a flexible body it usually means we have a flexible mind.

Dr. Blair Justice suggests that exercise is important for the body and the mind. Those who exercise regularly are less likely to get depressed. And those who are less likely to get depressed are less likely to get sick. When we exercise, two classes of chemicals (endorphins and enkephalins) are released by the hypothalamus in the brain. They act as natural pain killers. As well, they enhance activation of T cells and natural killer cells to destroy tumours.

Natural Killer cell

It is important to note that severe exercise, such as running a marathon, has been found to depress the immune system. This has been reflected in increased frequency of illnesses contracted in the hours following severe activity.

Before exercising consult your doctor. There are different kinds of exercise and its important to get the right kind for your body.

Sleep

In chapter two, we discovered that when the parasympathetic nervous system is stimulated it prepares the body for more sedentary activities such as sleep. Since it stimulates rest and repair, parasympathetic function must predominate before healing takes place. So sleep allows your body, including the immune system, the time it needs to regenerate and heal. Your organs go through cycles during a twenty four hour period. Sometime between 9 p.m. and 7 a.m. your body needs rest to allow your energy to be concentrated on regeneration. Be aware of your body's needs. You may need more sleep when your body is dealing with stressors.

Meditation

Meditation may mean different things to different people. Basically it is time out to listen to the silence. It is time to listen to the deepest part of you. This part of yourself is whole; your integrated body, mind, emotions and spirit.

Meditation decreases blood pressure and heart rate, regulates and slows down respiration, decreases the metabolic rate and reduces muscle tension. All of these aid the functioning of the immune system.

Studies have shown that people who meditate are healthier and more relaxed compared to non-meditators. Dr. David Orme-Johnson did a study that showed an 87% reduction in heart disease and nervous system disorders, a 55% reduction in tumour occurrences, and a 30% reduction in infectious diseases in meditators.

One of the few studies of the effectiveness of treatment of Post Traumatic Stress Disorder (a reaction to traumatic events such as war, child abuse, exposure to violence or natural catastrophe, etc.) found that meditation helped. Another study found that meditators, compared to control subjects, had a lower percentage of functional lymphocyte beta-adrenergic receptors. In other words, stress would not suppress the immune system in meditators as much as it would in non-meditators.

T suppressor

There are different kinds of meditation and you may need to search for one that suits your personality. There is active meditation, such as walking, and there is quiet meditation. There are simple meditative exercises you can do at home. Here's one you can try on for size...

(It may help for you to have a friend read this to you, or for you to tape your own voice, until you internalize it.) First, you need a quiet place where you will not be disturbed. Sit in a comfortable position, in comfortable clothes, and close your eyes (if you wish). Sitting in straight-backed chair, so your spine is straight, will enhance your breathing. Next, become aware of your breathing and as you breathe in, bring relaxation in. As you breathe out, let go any tightness or tension held in your muscles. Do this a few times. Imagine leaving your troubles and stresses in a box, knowing that you can come back to them after your meditation.

Right now, though your mind is alert, it is also passive, with your attention focused on your inner self. You may say to yourself, "I am relaxed" as you systematically relax your muscles from feet to head. If there is a particular area that holds more tension, feel free to spend extra time there. As you become more and more relaxed, and your breathing deepens, imagine you are in a comfortable, relaxing scene. Choose any scene you wish. Create a safe, loving space here for yourself— one that you can come back to time and time again. This is your place and no one can enter unless you invite them.

Feel your body respond to the relaxation. Notice all the sights, colours, sounds, etc. in your beautiful place. You can stay as long as you are comfortable. When you are ready to come back, gently return to a state of full mental alertness by slowly stretching. When you are ready, open your eyes and look around the room. Then you can get up slowly, feeling refreshed, energized and alert.

If this did not work for you, (or if it did, and you want more), remember that there are books, audio and visual tapes, as well as classes available, which provide instruction or further examples of meditation. Until definitive research shows that one particular kind of meditation is best for improving immune function or health, you can decide for yourself what feels best to you.

Meditation is very effective if practised on a regular basis. See if you can make it part of your daily schedule. Your immune system will appreciate it!

Relaxation

In the meditation section I suggested relaxing your muscles and saying I am relaxed. Relaxing physically is one of the basic ways to allow your body to heal. Using meditation is one way to relax. There are other ways to relax such as walking, puttering in the garden, reading, listening to music or taking a break from what you are doing.

Relaxation by itself has been shown to be an effective way to reduce feelings such as anxiety, depression, anger, or fear. It reduces muscular tension and muscle spasms. Relaxation has been effective in the treatment of headaches, insomnia, ulcers, and many other ailments. During relaxed states the brain produces alpha waves, which are associated with feelings of well-being, heightened awareness, creativity and openness to positive suggestions.

T helper

Janice Kiecolt-Glaser at Ohio State University found that when medical students were taught relaxation exercises, their helper T cells increased. Kiecolt-Glaser and her immunologist husband Ron Glaser have found that relaxation therapy has improved immune function in the elderly. Other studies have shown that stress hormones decrease after relaxation. Dr. Blair Justice says because our immune defenses tend to weaken when we generate stress hormones, relaxation exercises may be one way to keep our resistance up.

Laughter

Laughter, the best medicine, seems to enhance immune functioning. It reduces immune suppressors (like epinephrine –a hormone, and cortisol–a steroid). Laughter can release endorphins (our body's natural pain killers and natural high). When we laugh we massage all the internal organs in the body. It can reduce depression, ease tension, help us communicate better and invites and maximizes the learning process. It inspires creativity.

Norman Cousins, in *Anatomy of an Illness*, tells how he cured himself of a crippling and often-fatal rheumatoid condition with laughter and Vitamin C.

Want to improve your health? Start asking if your friends and colleagues have heard any good jokes lately, and try to pass a few more on to others. Learn to play. Read funny books and watch funny shows. Listen to your favourite comedians. Laugh at your foibles. Remember–nobody's perfect. In your imagination turn anxiety-laden situations into funny ones. Laugh your way to good health.

Network Of Friends

Having people around who provide friendship, feedback, support and caring is one of the best resources you can have. These support systems can be at work, home or play. The ones at home are built in while at work and play you will need to choose who you want on your team. We need to support each other. This support gives us a better self image, increases our

B plasma cell

self esteem and self confidence. When we feel love for ourselves it is easier to love and support others. Our enhanced sense of emotional well-being invigorates our physical bodies in many ways including boosting immune system power.

It has been reported that when we feel love (self-love or love for others), the production of antibodies increases, often dramatically. Conversely, investigators have discovered low levels of natural killer cells in lonely students and in some residents of nursing homes who felt abandoned by their families.

Mental/Emotional

A healthy mental attitude helps keep the immune system healthy. The body is a series of complex systems, each interacting with the other. The mind is the master of all these systems. It is one of the keys to health. The mind has the power to regulate all bodily functions and has the ability to manufacture many chemicals that make us feel good. The body and emotions are the servants of mind; they respond to our thoughts. The body also keeps score when we repress our emotions. So it is important to work on keeping our thoughts free of old negative beliefs, attitudes, decisions, memories, language patterns or emotional backlog.

Studies done with people with multiple personalities demonstrate how strongly belief systems affect our bodies. Dr. Bennett Braun has studied people with multiple personalities and discovered that when victims of this disorder shift character, their bodies shift along with them. Braun reported two patients who experienced allergic responses to citrus juice and cats respectively in some personalities. But when other personalities came out and took charge, the allergic reactions stopped immediately. Another multiple suffering a severe asthma attack was seen at an emergency department. When she switched to a personality which did not suffer from asthma, all symptoms disappeared, leaving an incredulous emergency doctor who could not believe what he had just witnessed. Although multiples experience themselves as having more than one person inside, this belief is mistaken; the personalities are parts of one person. But these cases illustrate that what we believe can have a profound effect on our immune systems.

Generally, our society does not encourage us to express emotions or feelings openly, so we find it difficult to express ourselves. We tend to keep our emotions locked up inside us. As well as impairing the functioning of the immune system, this can affect our physical bodies through energy blocks. This blocked energy can lead to tension in the body. Eventually this leads to physical pain, and if the block stays there long enough it can lead to illness. Different kinds of therapy can release these energy blocks. Through therapy people can learn to identify their blocked emotions and express them in a safe and supportive environment.

Therapy with a psychotherapist who is willing to help you explore traumatic events in your life, such as a childhood history of sexual, physical, or emotional abuse, can improve your physical health. Talking about these events improves immune functioning.

James Pennebaker has done research which established that disclosing traumas improved health. This has been shown to be true by other researchers. For example, self-help groups for adult female survivors of childhood sexual abuse resulted in significantly fewer health problems.

Macrophage

If therapy is not available, research shows that writing about traumatic events can improve immune system functioning.

In 1986, Pennebaker and Beall reported a remarkable effect of a brief cathartic treatment on health. Specifically, subjects who wrote descriptions of their feelings about traumatic life events for 4 consecutive days subsequently had fewer health centre visits than did subjects in several control groups.

In 1988, Pennebaker, Kiecolt-Glaser, and Glaser repeated this study and obtained the same results. In addition, they extended the previous work by taking blood samples from all their subjects, before, immediately after, and 6 weeks after the four day experiment. The blood was measured for immune system response. Immune functioning improved for the group which wrote about traumas, compared to the superficial topic group. Health improved too. The effect was most pronounced for those who had previously held back about their trauma. And although the effect was most obvious right after the experiment, it was also evident six weeks later. Pennebaker believes that writing about the trauma helps because it enhances understanding and insight, as well as providing emotional release.

Pennebaker advises that individuals who want to write to improve immune function, experiment with topics and determine what works best for them individually. He adds these guidelines:

Write about what currently is bothering you, not necessarily past traumas. Describe your deepest thoughts and feelings about what happened. Don't worry about spelling, grammar, etc., and use repetition if nothing new comes. Write whenever you feel you want or need to. If you can find somewhere unique to write, it probably enhances the process. Pennebaker recommends keeping your writing entirely private so you need feel no pressure to protect yourself or anyone else from how you feel and think. Write continuously for 15 minutes a day. It's not unusual if you feel sad or depressed for an hour or more after writing. If you feel uncomfortable writing, talking into a tape recorder for 15 minutes a day can be as beneficial. Don't hold back, let yourself go.

Visualization Or Imagery

Visualization or imaging is an imaginative technique - the ability to create an idea, or mental picture in your mind. In creative visualization, you use your imagination to create a clear image or picture of something you wish. Visualization and forming positive mental images can be practised to reduce certain stress-related illnesses.

Dr. Carl Simonton and Stephanie Matthews Simonton are well known for their work in the field of visualization. They have established a Cancer Counselling Research Centre in Dallas, Texas, where they guide their cancer patients in visualization as part of their treatment. The key to the success of their treatment techniques is the underlying belief that surviving cancer depends more on the patient's state of mind than on his or her physical condition.

In their book *Getting Well Again*, the Simontons, along with James Creighton, describe studies they undertook to complement traditional cancer treatment. After four years, 25 out of 159 *terminal* cancer patients, who used visualization as part of their regular therapy, were alive and improving.

Sceptics with a scientific background can rightly claim that there may be other explanations for these results. While it is true that *unknown factors* may explain the Simontons' successes, it is possible that they are factors related to visualization and immune system improvements. H.R Hall of Case Western Reserve University School of Medicine, reviewed evidence relating to voluntary immune system control. He believes that the successful voluntary alteration of one's immune functioning is complex. He found these factors may influence visualization:

- the importance of prior experience in self-regulation
- the role of practice
- the ability to become relaxed and reduce sympathetic arousal
- the importance of the nature and content of images

- the complex role of hypnosis and hypnotizability
- the importance of individual differences
- the aspect of the immune system you try to alter

Hall's work suggests that these (or other, as yet unrecognized) variables may be associated with visualization and voluntary influence on the immune system. Whether or not this explains the success of the Simontons awaits further scientific research. Meanwhile, it is important to note that I have found no scientific evidence that visualization is harmful.

Some authorities in the field of cancer treatment have also expressed concern that social pressure on cancer patients may lead them to attempt heroic responses against their true wishes. Another concern is that these techniques are offering false hope. On the other hand, consider that 100% of the Simontons' patients are reported to have been medically incurable. And isn't it up to each individual to decide what treatment is best for them in such circumstances, and to what extent they desire to fight for this? No one is offering guarantees, but these other options do no harm if they complement traditional medicine. And what if they help?

In 1987, Jasnoski and Kugler studied relaxation, imagery, and changes in the immune system. They found that subjects doing relaxation alone, and relaxation with imagery, had a higher level of one particular antibody than did the control group. This study suggests that relaxation alone might account for immune system improvements. However, visualization was done only once. Several studies reported below suggest that repeating imagery over time has a more pronounced effect than a one-time attempt. Nevertheless, the study does support the idea that relaxation helps improve one aspect of immune functioning.

In 1990, R. Zachariae and colleagues at the Institute of Psychology, University of Aarhus, in Denmark studied relaxation, guided imagery, and cellular immune function in normal healthy subjects. Over 10 days, 10 healthy subjects received one hour-long relaxation procedure, and one combined relaxation-and-guided-imagery procedure. The experimenters instructed subjects to imagine their immune systems becoming very effective. Even though no major changes in many immune cells could be demonstrated, a significant increase in natural killer function was demonstrated. The authors suggest that relaxation and guided imagery might have a beneficial effect on immune defense.

Dr. Nicholas Hall, at George Washington Medical Centre in Washington, D.C., found that cancer patients can increase their T cells by following a regime of guided imagery–visualizing their immune systems being turned on in the same way Olympic athletes prepare for competitions by thinking through every motion. Monthly testing of the patients' blood, over an 18-month period, provided scientific proof that people can use thoughts to increase immune cell activity, possibly improving defenses against infections to which cancer patients are prone, even if their tumours are unchanged.

Jeanne Achterberg showed that cell-specific mental imagery can effect neutrophil or lymphocyte cell counts. Her subjects (30 of them) were randomly placed in two groups. Six weeks of training helped the subjects to visualize the location, movement and structure of either neutrophils or lymphocytes. Music was used to facilitate the visualization. One group visualized changes in neutrophils; the other group visualized lymphocytes. White blood cell counts were measured before and after the final imagery session. The result was a statistically significant change in lymphocytes for the lymphocyte-visualizing group (but no change in their neutrophil levels). And for the neutrophil group, neutrophil levels changed, but lymphocyte levels did not, once again at levels unlikely to result from chance. This research is consistent with the view that measured immune system changes are cell-specific. It suggests that imagery, not relaxation, influences immune functioning.

Achterberg and colleagues at Southern Methodist University in Dallas, Texas, refined the study outlined above. College students with normal medical histories were randomly placed in one of three groups. The first group participated in short educational training on the production of IgA. Then, they were tested on salivary IgA before and after listening to a tape of imagery instructions with music designed to enhance imagery. Subjects in the second group listened to the same music, but received no formal training on the immune system, to see if the music had a placebo effect which might account for any results. The third group acted as a control.

The first two groups combined (the treatment groups) yielded significantly greater increases in IgA over the control group. It also appears likely that the imagery itself was effective in influencing immune functioning; Group 1 (imagery) was significantly higher than Group 2 (music only) in antibody production. This provides more support for the idea that imagery can improve immune functioning. It also raises the question of why music seems to help, and whether some kinds of music are better than others in helping the immune system.

Taken together, this research certainly suggests that some aspects of immune system can be influenced through visualization. It will take many more controlled studies to establish to what degree this is true and to convince the medical establishment. However, it seems to me that there would be no harm in visualizing changes in immune system functioning which would enhance your health. If you are suffering from a life threatening illness and would like to use visualization, you have the option of asking your doctor whether visualization would be harmful. For many people such reassurance from their doctor would be important before proceeding. Even if your doctor is sceptical, his or her assurance that visualization can do no harm is important. Your doctor may also be able to suggest specific immune system changes that would promote health in someone with your specific health difficulty.

How To Visualize

Visualization involves creating a safe internal space, similar to what you created when you went through the meditation exercise. It is important to be relaxed and go inside yourself. It usually helps to close your eyes, although some people can visualize quite well with eyes open. Next, become aware of your breathing and as you breathe in, bring relaxation in. As you breathe out, let go any tightness or tension held in your muscles. Do this a few times. Relax your muscles. Empty your mind of unwanted thoughts. Feel the relaxation and enjoy the release of tension. The more relaxed you are, the easier it is to visualize. Focus your attention on your inner self. Create a safe, loving space for yourself.

It is important to use this approach with an open mind. If you decide that it must work, and it does not, you will have set yourself up for disappointment. If you decide it can't work, it probably won't. It will probably work best if you keep an open mind and adopt an attitude of, "Let's try it and see what happens".

Visualization can work when you have the desire to change something and the belief that you can change. Use the inten-

B memory cell

tion to heal, focus on your desire, and see it as already existing in the present.

Many people feel they can not visualize. However, I find that everyone visualizes, whether you know it or not. Most people experience visualizations through dreaming at night, in day-dreams, remembering a past experience, or thinking of someone you know. The minority who persist and do not seem to be able to see pictures are often able to have a sense, or a sensation, which seems to work just as well, even if there is no visualization.

Visualization involves all the senses. When you visualize, feel, taste, smell, hear and see what you want. Switch to different senses. Use a lot of detail. Add movement and depth. Add style; you can make the pictures realistic, cartoon-like or impressionistic. Include appropriate emotions if needed.

When you see something, notice the colour, shade, shape, size, intensity, and distance. Observe clarity, focus, location, movement, and stillness. See density, speed, contrast, brightness, duration, perspective, angle, position, and texture. Is it dimensional, or flat? Is it in the foreground or background? Is it a movie, or slides? And are you in the picture, or watching what is going on?

When you hear something, notice the tone, tempo, volume, location, and direction. Listen for timbre, pitch, frequency, duration, intensity, distance, and rhythm. Is there a voice? Whose voice? Are there sounds, or words? Are the sounds inside, or outside you?

When you feel something, notice the temperature, texture, pressure, weight, and movement. Sense the location, moisture, duration, intensity, size, shape, and frequency. If there is pain, is it sharp, aching, burning, tearing, pulling, pushing, squeezing, ripping, or stinging. Is it internal or external? Notice internal sensations, nausea, hunger, fatigue, and the distinct bodily sensations associated with emotions such as fear, anger, depression or excitement. Sense your body's movement and position in space.

When you smell something, notice what kind of odour - strong or delicate, aromatic, pungent, or fragrant. Does it bring back any memories or change your mood?

When you taste something, notice if it's sweet, sour, bitter, or salty. Is it pungent, spicy, astringent, chalky, warm, or cool? Is there a particular flavour? What is it?

Now imagine that you are holding a lemon. Roll it around in your hand, and feel its texture. Notice the temperature. What colour is it? What shape is it? What size is it? Is it firm, or does it give a little? Now, cut the lemon in half with a knife. Does the knife cut through the lemon easily, or is there some resistance? Does the oil on the rind smell? Does the juice have any odour? Now bring the lemon half up to your mouth. Do you feel your mouth water as you look at the lemon? Now, taste it. What happens to your mouth as you taste it. What does it taste like? Do your lips pucker?

If you could see, feel, taste or smell the lemon, you were visualizing. Psychologist Erik Peper showed that 50 percent of a group of untrained people will salivate when led through a detailed visualization of a lemon. Paul Eckman, another psychologist at the University of California, found that mimicking an emotion influences your body in exactly the same way as actually experiencing the emotion.

Visualization can be used in combination with affirmations to help give you improved immune system functioning. Affirmations are strong, positive thoughts that you deliberately place in your mind. An affirmation is a way of directing your unconscious to help you achieve your goals—a method of creating what you would like to have happen in your life. It is a way of changing negative self talk into positive action. Affirmations can neutralize negativity. To create your affirmations you need to articulate the ultimate desired result, use present tense, affirm only in the positive, keep it simple but specific, and don't put a time limit on it.

Examples of affirmations are: "I am healthy, energetic and full of vitality. Everything I conceive and believe, I achieve. The present is the point of power. I have the power to produce perfect results in every area of my life. I have unlimited potential. I improve with age. I eat only those foods which are nutritious. I love exercising my body and keeping myself fit. Every cell in my body now functions in a perfect, healthy manner. Every night my sleep is restful and healing. I have the courage to experience and express my feelings. I am now becoming all that I was created to be. My inner wisdom guides me to make right decisions. Every part of my life has purpose and meaning."

You now have another tool to help you feel more in control of your own healing—to access your healing potential within. The most powerful visualization exercises are those that are individually crafted to include the new affirmations that you want to assimilate. For some of you, it might mean imagining the multiplication of T cells, B cells, and macrophages or for others your images may be totally symbolic. There is no right or wrong way; it is simply a matter of personal preference.

You can use your new information to visualize the immune system characters working with you to aid you in your healing of an existing illness or disease. If you are well, you can also visualize this way to promote continuing good health.

Dr. Nicholas Hall, when working with patients doing visualizations, noted that the patients selected their own images. One patient, who could not bring himself to kill anything, even cancer cells that might kill him, imagined his body as a garden where he watered and nourished flowers (white cells) and ignored weeds (cancer cells).

Many research studies done by psychologists in recent years have demonstrated the value of mental practice, that is, the value of visualizing an upcoming situation without any gross muscular movement. The classic article on mental practice, reported in Research Quarterly by the Australian psychologist Alan Richardson, concerned the effects of visualization on the free-throw scores of basketball players.

The study involved three groups of students chosen at random, none of whom had ever practised visualization. The first group practised free throws every day for twenty days. The second group made free throws on the first and twentieth days, with no practice in between. The third group also made free throws on the first and last days, but in addition, they spent twenty minutes a day imagining sinking baskets. As in the external world, when these students (mentally) missed, they tried to correct their aim on the next shot. The first group who actually practised, improved 24% between the first and last day. The second group, who had done no practice of any kind, did not improve at all. The third group, who visualized throwing the ball through the basket, improved 23%. Similar

Macrophage

studies involving dart throwing and other athletic activities show the same kind of results.

Our bodies react to mental images in the same way they react to the external world. The American physiologist, Edmund Jacobson, has done studies which show that when a person imagines running, small but measurable amounts of contraction actually take place in the muscles associated with running. The same neurological pathways are excited by imagined running as by actual running. In this sense, the nervous system cannot tell the difference between a well imagined thought (visualization) and reality. If you can imagine it clearly, your nervous system is experiencing it just as though you were doing it physically.

In 1991, in an investigative report about the relationship between induced emotional states and immune system changes, Zachariae and his colleagues studied the effect of brief, hypnotically induced emotional states on chemical stimulation of monocytes. (Monocytes are immature macrophages.) The results showed statistically significant differences in monocyte activity between angry and depressed emotional states. The depressed state exhibited a decreased chemical stimulation index compared with the angry state. The happy, relaxed emotional state also showed quite a statistically significant increase compared to the angry and depressed state.

The mind responds to and records a clearly visualized experience in the same manner as it would record an actual event. Any feelings or emotions associated with the visual are also recorded. In the study by Zachariae, we saw that emotions can affect immune system activity. We need to be aware that our negative self-talk or visualizing negative outcomes, can have an impact on our body functions. We need to corral our imagination and use it for creating positive outcomes. Your imagination can help you visualize yourself as you could be. If you can mentally conceive it and believe it, eventually you can achieve it.

Recently, I rid myself of a life-long cat allergy. While it wasn't life threatening, it was very bothersome. If I visited friends with a cat, within half an hour I was congested and sneezy. There seemed to be some correlation between my allergy and cats' attraction to me, because they constantly made a bee-line for me, too.

First, I looked at the causes of the allergy layer by layer. I became conscious of my belief system so I could change it. Then

I went into meditation, or a quiet space and visualized my eosinophils, basophils, neutrophils and macrophages. All these cells would be the first line of defense against cat hair. I talked to them about all the *bad guys* they had to deal with on a daily basis, and asked them if they would like to deal with only life- threatening invaders. They seemed to like the idea. So I told them they didn't need to attack cat hair any more. I did this two days in a row. By the end of the week the cat allergy was no more. To date, my immune system is enjoying only being responsible for life threatening foreign invaders. And I'm enjoying the company of cats as much as they enjoy me.

The secret to all visualization and imagery techniques, no matter how symbolic or literal, is to imagine your desired results as if they have already happened. This simple point is the secret of success. Whatever you hold in your mind's eye long enough, clearly enough and without doubt is more likely to become real. It also seems to help if you adopt a playful attitude; when you play you probably relax and let go and focus on enjoyment more than performing or getting it just right. Visualizing as if you have accomplished the reality you want, and doing this in a playful way, may be a new way for you to encourage your immune system. Have fun!

Summary

It is important not to blame yourself for being sick; concentrate on getting well. This chapter has introduced you to some basic friends of the immune system. There are many more. Wholistic health magazines and health food stores in your area will provide other resources. Using these resources, while working with your doctor, can enhance your healing process and your health.

Chapter 9

USING YOUR OWNER'S MANUAL: PUTTING IT ALL TOGETHER

You now have basic information about the immune system, and some of its enemies and friends. Now what?

There was a very religious man who lived in the outskirts of a village located in a valley. He kept to himself except on Sunday, when he went to church. One day there was a huge rain storm. A few days later the rain was still coming down and the village was beginning to flood. The villagers knew it was time to leave. A group of them went by the old man's house and asked him to join them. He refused, saying, "I am a good person and God will save me. Go on without me." Reluctantly they did.

The flooding continued. More people were evacuated, this time by row boat. Some rescuers went by the man's house. He was living on the upper level of his house at this point. As the row boat went by his window they urged him to get in. Once again he refused, saying, "God knows my devotion to Him, so He will save me." They went on to see if there were any others who needed to be rescued.

The flooding continued. The man's house was completely covered by water except his chimney. That was where he sat, praying. A helicopter went by looking for any other victims of this disaster. They saw him and let down a rope ladder and through a loud speaker said, "Climb up to safety." He yelled back, "God knows I'm a believer and I know He will save me." The helicopter finally left without him.

The flooding continued and the man drowned. When he got to the Pearly Gates, he demanded to see God. After a short wait, God appeared and the irritated man said: "I've been devoted to you all my life and you didn't save me. Why?". God answered: "My son, I gave you three chances and you refused my help."

In this story, human responsibility is not banished simply because of spiritual faith. Spiritual energy is always available to us, anytime we are open to it. We need to be aware of the mysterious way it works. The story also exemplifies our responsibility as humans to look after ourselves in the earthly realm. We are all inter-connected; if we work together we can heal ourselves and the planet.

My hope is that with more understanding about what goes on internally during the healing process, all of us will respect our immune systems and therefore respect ourselves. Also, I hope we can all feel more like active participants in our healing, with more choices. I hope that you will remember your immune system's friends and enemies the next time you become ill, or want to promote health and positive change in your body. Even if you make one change—add a friend or delete an enemy, your immune system will be supported.

We have some control over our healing processes, by assisting our innate healing ability. We can do this by washing a cut to allow the body to heal. Or, we can involve the mind, and consciously help the body heal. Once we involve our conscious mind, we need to believe in whatever healing treatment we've chosen. In my experience, that belief needs to be aligned with our unconscious core beliefs, otherwise the healing treatment will not work, or it will take longer. So it is important to examine our belief systems.

Our minds are powerful—perhaps more powerful than we think. It is clear that our beliefs can profoundly influence our physical bodies. If it is healing we desire, then we need to become emotionally involved with it, see it clearly, persist through action, expect and believe it to happen.

A root word for healing means *whole*, and also *holy*. Thus, to be healed is to be whole, at one with the universe. To be healed, our physical, mental, emotional and spiritual parts of our body must be in balance. Balance means being in touch with the ebb and flow of life. We are constantly experiencing change. Illness or disease are signals from within and give us an opportunity to look at and understand ourselves. We need to look beyond the symptoms and treat the causes.

Healing is a very complex subject, just as human beings are very complex. When I experience the death of friends, family or clients, I am reminded of the intangible life force, our essence, our purpose, our universal or spiritual connection and the things we don't understand. Even if we don't understand all aspects of healing, we can still use all the healing tools available to us.

We still don't have all the answers about immune system functioning and I have spared you some of the greater complexities of the subject. As you read this book, knowledge about the immune system continues to grow by leaps and bounds. As that knowledge changes, some of the statements in this book will obviously need revising. The main characters will remain the same and they may gain some new cousins as researchers find out more about our immune systems.

For the most part, the immune system works with other systems to maintain stability and balance within, preserving our most precious possession, vibrant health. It is abundantly obvious that we do have a miraculous and powerful defense system that nature has created for us. Let's do everything we can to help it take care of us.

REFERENCES

Abernathy, E. *How the immune system works*. American Journal of Nursing. v87, p456-9, April, 1987.

Abrahamson, E. M.; Pezet, A. W. *Body, Mind, and Sugar*. New York: Pyramid Communications, Inc. 1975.

Achterberg, J. *Imagery in Healing*. Boston, MA: New Science Library, Shambhala Publications, Inc. 1985.

Airola, P. *Are You Confused?* Phoenix, AZ: Health Plus Publishers. 1977.

Airola, P. *Health Secrets From Europe*. West Nyack, NY: Parker Publishing Company, Inc. 1983.

Airola, P. *How to Get Well*. Phoenix, AZ: Health Plus Publishers. 1974.

Airola, P. *Hypoglycemia: A Better Approach*. Phoenix, AZ: Health Plus Publishers. 1980.

Anderson Price, S.; McCarty Wilson, L. *Pathophysiology*. New York: McGraw-Hill Book Company. 1982.

Antoni, M.; Schneiderman, N.; Fletcher, M.; Goldstein, D.; Ironson, G.; Laperriere, A. *Psychoneuroimmunology and HIV-I*. Journal of Consulting and Clinical Psychology. v58(1), p38-49, 1990.

Assagioli, R. *Psychosynthesis*. New York: Penguin Books. 1965.

Baker, Elsworth F. *Man in the Trap*. New York: The Hearst Corporation. 1974.

Barnes, D. M. *Neuroimmunology sits on broad research base*. Science. v237, p1568-9, September 25, 1987.

Barrett, J. T. *Text Book of Immunology*, St. Louis, MI: The C.V. Mosby Company, 1988.

Basmajian, J. *Primary Anatomy*. Baltimore, MD: Williams & Wilkins. 1982.

Beck, D. and J. *The Pleasure Connection*. San Marcos, CA.: Synthesis Press. 1987.

Benson, H.; Klipper, M. *The Relaxation Response*. New York: The Hearst Corporation. 1975.

Berger, S. M. *Dr. Berger's Immune Power Diet*. New York: New American Library. 1985.

Berkow, R. (Ed.-in-Chief) *The Merck Manual of Diagnosis and Therapy*. Rahway, NJ: Merck & Co., Inc. 1982.

Bertherat, T.; Bernstein C. *The Body Has Its Reasons*. New York: Random House, Inc. 1977.

Bieler, Henry G. *Food is Your Best Medicine*. New York: Vintage Books Edition. 1973.

Blake, R. *Mind Over Medicine*. London, England: Aurum Press Limited. 1987.

Blalock, J. E. *A molecular basis for bidirectional communication between the immune and neuroendocrine systems*. Physiological Reviews. v69, p1-32, January, 1989.

Bloch, G. *Body & Self*. Los Altos, CA: William Kaufmann, Inc. 1985.

Borysenko, J.; Rothstein, L. *Minding the Body, Mending the Mind*. New York: Addison-Wesley. 1987.

Bourbeau, L. *Listen to Your Best Friend Your Body*. Montreal, Que: Les Editions E.T.C. Inc. 1989.

Bower, B. *Personality linked to immunity (natural cell activity & MMPI scores)*. Science News. v130, p310, November 15, 1986.

Bower, B. *Questions of mind over immunity: scientists rethink the link between psychology and immune function*. Science News. v139, p216-17, April 6, 1991.

Bower, B. *Severe depression depresses immunity*. Science News. v127, p100, February 16, 1985.

Bower, B. *Emotion-immunity link in HIV infection*. Science News. v134, p116, August 20, 1988.

Bowman, T. A.; Goonewardene, I. M.; Pasatiempo, A. M. *Vitamin A deficiency decreases natural killer cell activity and interferon production in rats*. The Journal of Nutrition. v120, p1264-73, October, 1990.

Bricklin, M. (Ed.). *The Practical Encyclopedia of Natural Healing*. Emmaus, PA: Rodale Press. 1976.

Bricklin, M. (Ed.). *The Natural Healing Annual 1986*. Emmaus, PA: Rodale Press. 1986.

Bricklin, M.; Prevention Magazine; et al. (Ed.). *Positive Living and Health*. Emmaus, PA: Rodale Press. 1990.

Brown, R.; Price, R.; King, M.; Husband, A. *Interleukin-1 beta and muramyl dipeptide can prevent decreased antibody response associated with sleep deprivation*. Brain, Behavior, & Immunity. v3(4), p320-30, December, 1989.

Carter, A. *The Cancer Answer*. Scottsdale, AZ: A.L.M. Publishers. 1988.

Chopra, D. *Creating Health*. Boston, MA: Houghton Mifflin Company. 1991.

Chopra, D. *Quantum Healing*. New York: Bantam Books, Inc. 1990.

Coffey-Lewis, L. *Be Restored to Health*. Toronto, Ont: Bestsellers, Inc. 1982.

Cohn, Z.; Ding-E Young, J. *How Killer Cells Kill*. Scientific American. v258(1), p38-44, January, 1988.

Coleman, V. *Mind Power*. Covent Garden, London: Century Hutchinson Ltd, 1986.

Coons, P. M. *Psychophysiologic Aspect of Multiple Personality Disorder.* v1(1), p47-53, March, 1988.

Cousins, N. *Anatomy of an Illness.* New York: W. W. Norton & Company, Inc. 1979.

Cousins, N. *Head First.* New York: Penguin Books. 1989.

Crook, William G. *The Yeast Connection.* Jackson, TENN: Professional Books. 1986.

D'Adamo, J.; Richards, A. *One Man's Food is Someone Else's Poison.* New York: Richard Marek Publishers. 1980.

Dadd, Debra L. *Nontoxic & Natural.* Los Angeles, CA: Jeremy P. Tarcher, Inc. 1984.

Davis, M.; Robbins Eshelman, E.; McKay, M. *The Relaxation & Stress Reduction Workbook.* Oakland, CA: New Harbinger Publications. 1982.

De Vries, J. *Stress and Nervous Disorders.* Edinburgh, Scotland: Mainstream Publishing Company. 1989.

De Vries, J. *Viruses, Allergies and the Immune System.* Edinburgh, Scotland: Mainstream Publishing Company. 1988.

De Vries, J. *Cancer and Leukaemia: An Alternative Approach.* Edinburgh, Scotland: Mainstream Publishing Company. 1988.

Denning, M.; Phillips, O. *Creative Visualization: For the Fulfillment of Your Desires.* St. Paul, MN: Llewellyn Publications. 1985.

Diamond, John. *Your Body Doesn't Lie.* New York: Warner Books, Inc. 1979.

Diamond, H. and M. *Fit For Life.* New York: Warner Books, Inc. 1987.

Dixon, B. *Dangerous thoughts: how we think and feel can make us sick.* Science. v7, p62-6, April, 1986.

Donsbach, K.W. *Dr. Donsbach's Super Health*. Huntington Beach, CA: International Institute of Natural Health Sciences, Inc. 1980.

Dossey, L. *Space, Time & Medicine*. Boulder, CO: Shambhala Publications, Inc. 1982.

Dossey, L. *Recovering The Soul*. New York: Bantam Books. 1989.

Dufty, W. *Sugar Blues*. New York: Warner Books, Inc. 1976.

Dunlop, M. *Body Defenses*. Toronto, Ont: Irwin Publishing. 1987.

Dunn, A. J. *Nervous system-immune system interactions: an overview*. Journal of Receptor Research. v8(1-4), p.589-607, 1988.

Dychtwald, K. *Body-Mind*. New York: Jove Publications, Inc. 1981.

Epstein, G. *Healing Visualizations: Creating Health Through Imagery*. New York: Bantam Books, Inc. 1989.

Faelten, S.; *Prevention Magazine (Ed.). The Allergy Self-Help Book*. Emmaus, PA: Rodale Press. 1983.

Fanning, P. *Visualization For Change*. Oakland, CA.: New Harbinger Publications, Inc. 1988.

Feltman, J. (Ed.) *Hands-On Healing*. Emmaus, PA: Rodale Press. 1989.

Figge, F.; Sobotta, J. *Atlas of Human Anatomy*. New York: Hafner Publishing Company, Inc. 1965.

Figley, Charles R. (Ed.). *Trauma and Its Wake. Traumatic Stress Theory, Research, and Intervention*. New York: Brunner Mazel. 1986.

Fischer, W.L. *How To Fight Cancer & Win*. Vancouver, B.C.: Alive Books. 1987.

Fisher, Gregg C. *Chronic Fatigue Syndrome*. New York: Warner Books, Inc. 1989.

Forman. R. *How to Control Your Allergies*. New York: Larchmont Books. 1983.

Fox, A. and B. *Immune for Life*. Rocklin, CA.: Prima Publishing & Communications. 1990.

Fredericks, C. *Psycho-Nutrition*. New York: The Putnam Publishing Group. 1976.

Fredericks, C. *Carlton Fredericks' Nutritional Guide for the Prevention & Cure of Common Ailments & Diseases*. New York: Simon & Schuster, Inc. 1982.

Fredericks, C. *Carlton Fredericks' Program for Living Longer*. New York: Simon & Schuster, Inc. 1983.

Friedlander, Jr. M.P.; Phillips, T.M. *Winning the War Within*. Emmaus, PA.: Rodale Press. 1986.

Fronk, Ron L. *Creating a Lifestyle You Can Live With*. Springdale, PA: Whitaker House. 1988

Garrison, R.; Somer, E. *The Nutrition Desk Reference*. New Canaan, CT: Keats Publishing, Inc. 1985.

Gawain, S. *Creative Visualization*. New York: Bantam Books, Inc. 1978.

Gendlin, Eugene T. *Focusing*. New York: Bantam Books, Inc. 1982.

Gerber, R. *Vibrational Medicine*. Santa Fe, CA: Bear & Company. 1988.

Goldstein, R. A.; Fauci, A. S. *A new series on the revolution in immunology*. The New England Journal of Medicine. v316, p1338-9, May 21, 1991.

Golos, N.; Golos Golbitz, F. *Coping With Your Allergies*. New York: Simon & Schuster, Inc. 1986.

Good, R. A.; Lorenz, E. *Nutrition, immunity, aging, and cancer.* Nutrition Reviews v46, p62-7, February, 1988.

Green, E. and A. *Beyond Biofeedback.* New York: Delacorte Press. 1977.

Grossinger, R. *Planet Medicine.* Boulder, CO: Shambhala Publications, Inc. 1982.

Guyton, A.C. *Textbook of Medical Physiology.* Philadelphia, PA: W. B. Saunders Company. 1981.

Haas, Elson, M. *Staying Healthy With the Seasons.* Berkeley, CA: Celestial Arts. 1981.

Hall, H.R. *Research in the area of voluntary immunomodulation: complexities, consistencies and future research considerations.* International Journal of Neuroscience. v47(1-2), p81-9, July, 1989.

Hall, N. R.; Goldstein, A. L. *Thinking well: the chemical links between emotions and health.* The Sciences. v26, p34-40, March/April 1986.

Hammer, S. *The mind as healer.* Science Digest. v92, p46-9, April, 1984.

Hanson, P. *The Joy of Stress.* Toronto, Ont: Hanson Stress Management Organization. 1986.

Hay, L. *You Can Heal Your Life.* Santa Monica, CA: Hay House. 1984.

Hoffer, A.; Walker, M. *Orthomolecular Nutrition: New Lifestyle for Super Good Health.* New Canaan, CT: Keats Publishing, Inc. 1978.

Howe, Phyllis S. *Nutrition for Practical Nurses.* Philadelphia, PA: W. B. Saunders Company. 1969.

Hunt, D. *No More Cravings.* New York: Warner Books, Inc. 1987.

Jacob, S.W.; Francone, C.A. *Structure and Function in Man*. Philadelphia, PA: W. B. Saunders Company. 1974.

Jasnoski, M.L.; Kugler, J. *Relaxation, imagery, and neuroimmunomodulation*. Annals of the New York Academy of Sciences. v496, p722-30, 1987.

Justice, B. *Who Gets Sick: Thinking and Health*. Houston, TX.: Peak Press. 1987.

Kanigel, R. *Where mind and body meet: the immune system appears to be very much involved with—if not under the control of— the central nervous system*. Mosaic (Washington, D.C.). v17, p52-60, Summer 1986.

Keith, V.; Gordon, M. *The How to Herb Book*. Pleasant Grove, UT: Mayfield Publications. 1984.

Kenyon, Julian N. *21st Century Medicine*. Wellingborough, Northhamptonshire: Thorsons Publishers Ltd. 1986.

Khalsa, G.S.; Briggs, G. *Stress Away: The Way to Relax*. Toronto, Ont: Gage Publishing Ltd. 1979.

Kiecolt-Glaser, J.; Glaser, R. *Psychological influences on immunity: Implications for AIDS*. American Psychologist. v43(11), p892-8, 1988.

Kirschmann, J.; Dunne L. *Nutrition Almanac*. New York: McGraw-Hill Book Company. 1984.

Kissner, R.; Bognar, C.; Cassidy, W. et al. *The Trauma in Our Midst: A Study of SARA - "Sexual Assault Recovery Anonymous"*. Surrey, B.C: SARA. 1988.

Kloss, J. *Back to Eden*. Santa Barbara, CA: Woodbridge Press Publishing Co. 1975.

Lambley, P. *The Psychology of Cancer*. London, England: Macdonald & Company Ltd. 1987.

LeShan, L. *Cancer as a Turning Point*. Hammondsworth, England: The Penguin Group. 1990.

LeShan, L. *How to Meditate*. New York: Bantam Books, Inc. 1986.

LeShan, L. *You Can Fight For Your Life*. New York: M. Evans and Company, Inc. 1977.

Lewith, G. T.; Kenyon, J. N. *Clinical Ecology*. Wellingborough, Northhamptonshire: Thorsons Publishers Ltd. 1985.

Lockhart, R.; Hamilton, G.; Fyfe, F. *Anatomy of the Human Body*. London, England: Faber and Faber Ltd. 1959.

Longgood, W. *The Poisons in Your Food*. New York: Pyramid Communications Inc. 1970.

Lowen, A. *Bioenergetics*. New York: Penguin Books. 1981.

Lowen, A. *The Betrayal of the Body*. Toronto, Ont: Collier-Macmillan Canada Ltd. 1969.

Maddox, J. *Immunology made accessible*. Nature. v310, p183, July 19, 1984.

Maddox, J. *Psychoimmunology before its time*. Nature. v309, p400, May 31, 1984. Discussion. v315, p103-4, May 9, 1985.

Martin, P. *Psychology and the immune system*. New Scientist. v114, p46-50, April 9, 1987.

Marwick, C. *As immune system yields its secrets, new strategies against disease emerge*. The Journal of the American Medical Association. v262, p2786-7, November 24, 1989.

Marx, J. L. *The immune system "belongs in the body"*. Science. v227, p1190-2, March 8, 1985.

Matsen, J. *Eating Alive*. Vancouver, B.C: Crompton Books. 1987.

McDougall, J. A. and M. A. *The McDougall Plan*. Piscataway, NJ: New Century Publishers, Inc. 1983.

McDougall, J. A. *McDougall's Medicine*. Piscataway, NJ: New Century Publishers, Inc. 1985.

Mendelsohn, Robert S. *Confessions of a Medical Heretic.* New York: Warner Books, Inc. 1980.

Michaud, E.; Anastas, L.; Prevention Magazine (Ed.). *Listen to Your Body.* Emmaus, PA: Rodale Press. 1988.

Miller, E. E. *Self Imagery.* Berkeley, CA: Celestial Arts. 1986.

Mills, P.; Schneider, R.; Hill, D.; Walton, K.; Wallace, R. *Beta-adrenergic receptor sensitivity in subjects practising transcendental meditation.* Journal of Psychosomatic Research. v34(1), p29-33, 1990.

Mindell, E. *Earl Mindell's New and Revised Vitamin Bible.* New York: Warner Books, Inc. 1985.

Mizel, S. B. *The Human Immune System.* New York: Simon & Schuster, Inc. 1986.

Moldofsky, H.; Lue, F. A.; Davidson, J. R.; Gorczynski, R. *Effects of sleep deprivation on human immune functions.* Faseb Journal. v3(8), p1972-7, June, 1989.

Montgomery, B.; Doran, R.; Lum-Doran, P.A. *Coping With Stress.* Toronto, Ont: Copp Clark Pitman Ltd. 1984.

Moody, R.A. Jr. *Laugh After Laugh: The Healing Power of Humor.* Jacksonville, Florida: Headwaters Press. 1978.

Morgan, B. and R. *Hormones.* Los Angeles, CA: Price Stern Sloan. 1989.

Muramoto, N. *Healing Ourselves.* New York: The Hearst Corporation. 1973.

Murphy, J. *The Power of Your Subconscious Mind.* Englewood Cliffs, N.J: Prentice-Hall, Inc. 1963.

Neale, J.; Cox, D.; Stone, A.; Valdimarsdottir, H. *The relation between immunity and health: Comment on Pennebaker, Kiecolt-Glaser, and Glaser.* Journal of Consulting and Clinical Psychology. v56(4), p636-7, 1988.

Newman, L. *Make Your Juicer Your Drug Store*. New York: Benedict Lust Publications. 1972.

Nossal, G. *Current concepts: Immunology; the basic components of the immune system*. The New England Journal of Medicine. v316, p1320-5, May 21, 1987.

Nuernberger, P. *Freedom From Stress*. Honesdale, PA: The Himalayan International Institute of Yoga Science and Philosophy Publishers. 1981.

Ornstein, R.; Sobel, D. *The Healing Brain*. New York: Simon & Schuster Inc. 1987.

Oyle, I. *Time Space & the Mind*. Berkeley, CA: Celestial Arts. 1976.

Padus, E.; Prevention Magazine (Ed.). *Your Emotions and Your Health*. Emmaus, PA: Rodale Press. 1986.

Pearsall, P. *Superimmunity*. New York: Ballantine Books. 1987.

Pelletier, K. R. *Holistic Medicine*. New York: Dell Publishing Co., Inc. 1979.

Pennebaker, James W. *Opening Up: The Healing Power of Confiding in Others*. New York: William Morrow & Company. 1990.

Pennington, S. *Healing Yourself: Understanding How Your Mind Can Heal Your Body*. Toronto, Ont: McGraw-Hill Ryerson Ltd. 1988.

Pert, C. *The material basis of emotions*. Whole Earth Review. No. 59, p106-11, Summer 1988.

Pestka, J. J.; Witt, M. F. *An overview of immune function*. Food Technology. v39, p83-90, February, 1985.

Potts, E.; Morra, M. *Understanding Your Immune System*. New York: Avon Books. 1986.

Randolph, T.G.; Moss, R. W. *Allergies: Your Hidden Enemy*. New York: Lippincott and Crowell. 1986.

Ratliff-Crain, J.; Kiecolt-Glaser, J.; Temoshok, L.; Tamarkin, L. *Issues in psychoneuroimmunology research*. Health Psychology. v8(6), p747-52, 1989.

Reckling, J.B.; Neuberger, G.B. *Understanding immune system dysfunction*. Nursing. v17, p34-6, September, 1987.

Reilly, Harold J.; Hagy Brod, R. *The Edgar Cayce Handbook for Health Through Drugless Therapy*. New York: Jove Publications, Inc. 1982.

Restak, R. M. *The Brain: The Last Frontier*. New York: Warner Books, Inc. 1979.

Rider, M.S.; Achterberg, J.; Lawlis, G.F.; Goven, A.; Toledo, R.; Butler, J.R. *Effect of immune system imagery on secretory IgA*. Biofeedback & Self Regulation. v15(4), p317-33, Dec. 1990.

Rider, M.S.; Achterberg, J. *Effect of music-assisted imagery on neutrophils and lymphocytes*. Biofeedback & Self Regulation. v14(3), p247-57, Sept. 1989.

Risenberg, D.E. *Can mind affect body defenses against disease?* The Journal of the American Medical Association. v256, p313+, July 18, 1986.

Robbins, J. *Diet For A New America*. Walpole, N.H.: Stillpoint Publishing. 1987.

Rosenber, S. A. *Adoptive Immunotherapy for Cancer*. Scientific American. p62-9, May, 1990.

Rossi, E. L. *The Psychobiology of Mind-Body Healing*. New York: W. W. Norton & Company, Inc. 1986.

Rowand, A. *Depression and the lymphocyte link*. Sciences News. v125, p341, June 2, 1984.

Rowland, D. *Balancing Body Chemistry*. Uxbridge, Ont: Canadian Nutrition Institute, Inc. 1986.

Royal, P. C. *Herbally Yours*. Provo, UT: Sound Nutrition. 1982.

Rusk, T. *Mind Traps*. Los Angeles, CA: Price Stern Sloan, Inc. 1988.

Samuels, M. *Seeing With the Mind's Eye: The History, Techniques and Uses of Visualization*. New York: Random House, Inc. 1975.

Schroeder, Henry A. *The Poisons Around Us*. New Canaan, CT: Keats Publishing, Inc. 1974.

Selye, H. *Stress Without Distress*. New York: The New American Library, Inc. 1975.

Shames, R.; Sterin, C. *Healing With Mind Power*. Emmaus, PA: Rodale Press. 1978.

Shapiro, S. *The mending mind*. Science Digest. v94, p62-5, March 1986.

Shealy, N. *90 Days to Self-Health*. Columbus, OH: Brindabella Books. 1987.

Sheinkin, D.; Schachter, M.; Hutton R. *Food, Mind & Mood*. New York: Warner Books, Inc. 1980.

Siegel, B. *Love, Medicine & Miracles*. New York: Harper & Row, Publishers, Inc. 1986.

Siegel. B. *Peace, Love & Healing*. New York: Harper & Row, Publishers, Inc. 1989.

Simeons, A.T.W. *Man's Presumptuous Brain*. New York: E. P. Dutton & Co., Inc. 1962.

Simonton, C.; Matthews-Simonton, S.; Creighton, J. *Getting Well Again*. New York: Bantam Books, Inc. 1978.

Singsank, David and Dennis. *Personal Lifeplan for Health & Fitness*. Madison, WI: American Health and Nutrition. 1983.

Smith, A. *The Body*. New York: Walker Publishing Company, Inc. 1968.

Stoff, J. A.; Pellegrino, C.R. *Chronic Fatigue Syndrome: The Hidden Epidemic*. New York: Harper & Row. 1990.

Stone, R. *Health Building*. Reno, NV: CRCS Publications. 1985.

Suzuki, D.; Thalenberg, E.; Knudtson, P. *David Suzuki Talks About AIDS*. Toronto, Ont: General Publishing Paperbacks. 1987.

Taub, Edward A. *Voyage to Wellness*. Orange, CA: Wellness America. 1988.

Thie, J. F. *Touch for Health*. Marina del Rey, CA: DeVorss & Company, Publishers. 1973.

Thurston, E. W. *The Parents' Guide to Better Nutrition for Tots to Teens (and Others)*. New Canaan, CT: Keats Publishing, Inc. 1976.

Tilden, J.H. *Toxemia Explained*. New Canaan, CT: Keats Publishing, Inc. 1981.

Topping, W. *Stress Release*. Bellingham, WA: Topping International Institute. 1985.

Trowbridge, J. P.; Walker, M. *The Yeast Syndrome*. New York: Bantam Books, Inc. 1986.

Tubesing, D.A. *Kicking Your Stress Habits*. New York: Penguin Books. 1981.

Turpin, G. (Ed.). *Handbook of Clinical Psychophysiology*. Toronto, Ont: Wiley Publishing. 1989.

Van De Graaff, K.; Rhees, R. *Human Anatomy and Physiology*. New York: McGraw-Hill Book Company. 1983.

Warmbrand, M. *The Encyclopedia of Health and Nutrition*. New York: Pyramid Communications, Inc. 1974.

Wechsler, R. *A new prescription: mind over malady (psychoneuroimmunology (PNI) links brain to immune system)*. Discover. v8, p50-3, February, 1987.

Weil, A. *Health and Healing*. Boston, MA: Houghton Mifflin Company. 1988.

Weil, A. *Natural Health, Natural Medicine*. Boston, MA: Houghton Mifflin Company. 1990.

Weksler, M. E. *Protecting the aging immune system to prolong quality of life*. Geriatrics v45, p72+, July, 1990.

Williams, R.J. *Biochemical Individuality*. Austin, TX: University of Texas Press. 1956.

Wolf, F.A. *The Body Quantum*. New York: MacMillan Publishing Company. 1986.

Wood, C. *How stress may predispose to disease*. New Scientist. v106, p31, July 4, 1985.

Woods Schindler. L.; U.S. Dept. of Health and Human Services. *Understanding the Immune System*. Bethesda, MD: National Institutes of Health; Publication No. 88-529. 1988.

Zachariae, R.; Kristensen, J.S.; Hokland, P.; Ellegaard, J.; Metze, E.; Hokland, M. *Effect of psychological intervention in the form of relaxation and guided imagery on cellular immune function in normal healthy subjects. An overview*. Psychotherapy & Psychosomatics. v54(1), p32-9, 1990.

Zachariae, R.; Bjerring, P.; Zachariae, C.; Arendt-Nielsen, L.; Nielsen, T.; Eldrup, E.; Larsen, C.S.; Gotliebsen, K. *Monocyte chemotactic activity in sera after hypnotically induced emotional states*. Scandinavian Journal of Immunology. v34(1), p71-9, July, 1991.

Zehr, A. *Dr. Albert Zehr's Healthy Steps to Maintain or Regain Natural Good Health*. Burnaby, B.C: Abundant Health Publishers. 1990.

Index

ABOUT THE AUTHOR

Charlene Day, Director of a personal development group, *The Day Company*, is a well-known consultant, author and educator. Her expertise in the areas of wellness, lifestyle counselling and stress management is the result of over 20 years of study and practice. Charlene is a Master Practitioner in Neuro-Linguistic Programming (NLP), a Registered Nutritional Consultant and holds a diploma in Social Work.

She integrates NLP, stress management, personal development, communication skills, specialized kinesiology, oriental philosophy, nutrition, meditation, creative visualization, wellness and empowerment into her consulting and private practice. She has the gift of blending the rational with the intuitive and she has a passionate belief that inspiring people to empower themselves is the first step toward a peaceful planet.

Currently, Ms. Day is a consultant to major corporations and educational institutions in the areas of wellness, lifestyle counselling and stress management.

Charlene Day is available for speaking engagements and seminars.

Contact:

> *Potentials Within*
> *Suite 1839*
> *5334 Yonge St.*
> *North York, Ontario M2N 6M2*

To order more books contact:

> *R & R Book Bar*
> *14800 Yonge Street*
> *Aurora Shopping Centre*
> *Aurora, Ontario L4G 1N3*
> *(416) 727-3300*
> *FAX (416) 727-2620*